Land Warfare: Brassey's New Battlefield
Weapons Systems and Technology Series
Volume 11

Powering War
Modern Land Force
Logistics

Land Warfare: Brassey's New Battlefield Weapons Systems
and Technology Series

Executive Editor: Colonel R G Lee OBE, Former Military Director of Studies,
Royal Military College of Science, Shrivenham, UK.

Editor-in-Chief: Professor Frank Hartley, Vice Chancellor, Cranfield Institute
of Technology, UK.

The success of the first series on Battlefield Weapons Systems and Technology
and the pace of advances in military technology have prompted Brassey's to
produce a new Land Warfare series. This series updates subjects covered in the
original series and also covers completely new areas. The new books are written
for military personnel who wish to advance their professional knowledge. In
addition, they are intended to aid anyone who is interested in the design,
development and production of military equipment.

Powering War

Modern Land Force Logistics

P. D. Foxton

BRASSEY'S (UK)
LONDON * NEW YORK

First English edition 1994

UK editorial offices:
Brassey's, 165 Great Dover Street, London SE1 4YA

Orders:
Marston Book Services, PO Box 87, Oxford OX2 ODT

USA orders: Macmillan Publishing Company, Front and Brown Streets, Riverside, NJ 08075

Distributed in North America to booksellers and wholesalers by the Macmillan Publishing Company, NY 10022

Library of Congress Cataloging in Publication Data
Available

British Library Cataloging in Publication Data
A catalogue record for this book is
available from the British Library

1 85753 053 5 Hardcover
1 85753 048 9 Flexicover

P.D. Foxton has asserted his moral right to be identified as author of this work

Typeset by Florencetype Ltd, Kewstoke, Avon
Printed and bound in Great Britain by
Butler & Tanner Ltd, Frome and London

Contents

Acknowledgements

It is customary in works of this kind to say that there are so many to thank that it is impossible to mention more than a few individuals. Or to say that someone might be missed inadvertently and thus it would be better to mention nobody. There are indeed a legion of people who have helped me, often at some cost to themselves in time. To them all I owe my thanks. I feel it only fair to list those who particularly gave of their time and their energy. Besides, it might make some of them buy the book.

Readers will note the preponderance of colonels and lieutenant colonels amongst those I have thanked. This is not as a result of some embryonic colonels' junta, but reflects the realities of military life. Majors run their armies and rarely have time to do anything else. The experience of lieutenant colonels is greater than the experience of majors. Besides, colonels and lieutenant colonels have staff to help them and thus have time to think.

For even soldiers sometimes think
Nay, Colonels have been known to reason –
And reasons, whether clad in pink,
Or red, or blue, are on the brink
(Nine cases out of ten) of treason.

Thomas Moore 1779–1852.
(Quoted in R. D. Heinl Jr's *Dictionary of Military and Naval Quotations*, Naval Institute Press, 1966.)

Doctors P. Griffith, C. Duffy and Mr N. de Lee whose knowledge and friendship fostered an amateur's interest in military history.

Brigadiers M F. John (late Royal Army Ordnance Corps) whose willingness to entertain debate so stimulated my own mind; A. C. D. Welch (late Royal Army Ordnance Corps) for permission to use his logistic winter warfare photographs and for his advice as a previous commanding officer of the Commando Logistic Regiment; A. Lyons (late Royal Army Ordnance Corps) who read and commented on the first draft.

Colonels H. Bentley Marchant (late Royal Corps of Transport) for his photographs of types of army transport, R. F. Macdonald (late Royal Pioneer Corps) for his comments on the labour function, B. McCandlish (late Royal Engineers (Postal and Courier Service)) for his comments on the postal section, G. Wilkinson (late Army Catering Corps) for his photographs on the catering function, A. D. Ball (late Royal Electrical and Mechanical Engineers) for his comments on the maintenance function.

Lieutenant Colonels M. Kerley, Royal Army Ordnance Corps, commanding officer of the Parachute Logistic Battalion for his photographs of airborne logistics; P Rossiter, Army Catering Corps for his comments on the catering function, N. D. A. Seymour, The Royal Scots Dragoon Guards (Carabiniers and Greys) for his photographs of logistic activities in the field, R. B. P. Smith Royal Army Ordnance Corps, for his photographs of types of ration packs and his help with fuel consumption figures and calorific values of various types of rations. A. Esquerre, French Army, for his help with the French Army's *Logistique Des Annees 90*.

Oberstleutnant H. G. Ziegler FRG, for his photographs of the German Army and his comments on the first draft of this book; Oberstleutnant K. Zeisig, for his German Army photographs; Lieutenant Colonel RE Zimmerman USA, for his comments on the first draft; Lieutenant Colonel JW Lewis USA, for his help with the organisation of modern US Army logistics; and Lieutenant Colonel M.G. Wood MBE RAOC, for his photographs of desert logistic activities.

Major J. Little, Royal Corps of Transport, who advised on the transport function. Captain M. Gilbertson, Royal Engineers (Postal and Courier Service), for his photographs of the postal function. Mr Gordon Wardle who drew the figures. A special word of thanks to Lieutenant Colonel A. Taylor, Royal Army Ordnance Corps who not only took over command of a battalion from me, and remained my friend, but also took that battalion on operations for the liberation of Kuwait and thus was able to advise me on desert logistic operations. As if this were not enough, he also read the first draft of this work.

Lastly I must thank Colonel G. Lee (late King's) without whose gentle encouragement and prodding of a reluctant amateur author this work would never have been written.

Preface

The military, like any other professional group, have their own language. Indeed, with its liberal use of acronyms, it can sound like no other language on earth. In this book, despite the extra space taken up and the repetition that results, attempts have been made to avoid this sort of militarese. Should they have failed, then the fault is mine and no-one else's.

The original aim of this book was to explain logistics in simplistic terms to those who would not actually practise logistics themselves but who would have the direction of, or would comment on, those that were. The target population was, therefore, basically civilian. As must often happen, the act of writing served to crystallise and develop my own thoughts and I fear that it has become somewhat more than this. Again, the fault is mine.

We are all products of our experience and the views expressed within this work are very much the product of my experience as a British Army logistic officer of many years. I hope that this sort of experience could be useful to others; hence this book. Similarly, it would be wrong for me to claim all the ideas and concepts within the book as purely mine. They are a result of what I have been taught, what I have practised and the discussions I have had with many professional colleagues and friends within and without the British Army and within the United Kingdom and abroad. I must, however, emphasise that the facts and opinions within this work are entirely my responsibility and do not imply endorsement by the Ministry of Defence of the United Kingdom or by any other agency.

Any work on 'modern' warfare runs the risk of straying into classified areas. Fortunately, especially in relation to the liberation of Kuwait in 1991, the military classify logistic facts less highly than others and a vast amount of information was released to the press. It is thus in the public domain and can be used in works such as this. Conversely, this book deals with logistics and there have been very few published works on the subject. Many of the facts and figures which relate to logistics appear nowhere other than in technical manuals which, while perhaps unclassified, are not available to the general public. Many of the facts and figures relate to my personal experience or knowledge and thus figure in no work that can be quoted. As a result, I considered using no footnotes at all. My academic friends rapidly convinced me that this was scholastic suicide; proving that it is not only the military for whom:

'Nothing so comforts the military mind as the maxim of a great but dead general.'

B. W. Tuchman; *The Guns of August*, 1962.

If, however, a figure or fact quoted in this work is not supported and does not appear self-evident I would be delighted to enter into correspondence on the subject. Indeed, such correspondence would at least show that somebody had read what I had written!

The use of the word 'logistics' has grown in both military and civilian usage over recent years. Its origins are American, as are so many seemingly simple one word statements that cover really rather complex ideas. Like so many things in man's understanding, it describes nothing new. Its constituents have been around as long as man has wanted to conduct complicated civilian or military operations. Like most good words, once coined, its general usage grew rapidly. It is now at the stage of being a 'Buzz-Word' or 'OK Cry'; a lot of people use it but few understand what it means.

It has to be said, too, that the subject is unattractive to the general reader. It has none of the romance or glamour of the more obvious military pursuits and rarely appeals to the romantic strain that is in all men. Reading lists of tonnages moved does not compare with reading of some famous charge. Yet probably the charge could not have taken place without the tonnages having been moved. Civilian business, with its hard-headed approach to much of life, recognises the importance of logistics; indeed, in the United Kingdom there is an Institute of Logistics, and no equipment programmes can be put to the US Congress without an Integrated Logistic Support plan being included.

It is the military who find it hardest to come to grips with logistics. In commerce logistics is an integral factor of every action. The military, who do not practise their trade fully in peace, are not so constrained. As plans are made and committed to paper, logistics could be a constraining factor and thus is often only paid lip service.

At one level this is understandable. Much of the military man's life and ambition revolves around concepts and abstract ideas. Some of the world's most famous military leaders have been those who by dint of sheer leadership could transform the morale and performance of armies without improving their soldiers' logistic state. The young Napoleon Bonaparte took over the starving and ragged French Army of Italy in 1796 and transformed it by virtue of his sheer presence and style. But a modern army is a mechanised one and it is difficult to motivate petrol-less engines. In the past, some of the great leaders have been great logisticians; arguably the greatest of them. In modern warfare there is no choice. The modern great general must also be a great logistician.

Yet, to some, logistics does have a fascination. There is the mathematical certainty of it, rather like a Mozart concerto. A combat officer might be taken by the sight of a squadron of tanks moving at high speed across country. A logistic officer will find that a racing column of carefully spaced heavy trucks will have the same effect. An artillery officer will be fiercely proud as he watches a battery deploy from the line of march to its firing position. So will a logistic officer as he watches a forward supply company pull off a main supply route into a staging area where it can set up to replenish a combat unit in trouble.

Explaining the fascination of logistics to someone who has not experienced it is rather like explaining music to someone who cannot hear. For a combat officer, a posting to a logistic appointment is something to be avoided. But many of those who become logisticians rise to the very highest appointments and all but a very few, like Saul on the road to Damascus, become even more logistically-minded than logisticians.

I had thought to call this work 'The Really Exciting Logistic Book'. But, being born to be led, I let myself be persuaded that this title lacked gravitas, hence the current rather worthy title. Although aimed at opinion-formers, I hope that some of my military colleagues might pick it up. Some of the younger ones might then become 'Pauls'. I hope so. For I remain convinced that a modern Great Captain cannot be so unless he is also a great logistician. Despite the break up of the Warsaw Pact there is no sign that the world of the future will be any more at peace than it is now. We shall continue to need defence forces and the men to command them. I hope that those who will have that honour will be Great Logisticians as well as Great Captains.

List of Plates

List of Figures

MAP SYMBOLS USED THROUGHOUT THIS BOOK

Size symbols

(rectangle)	Basic symbol for a military unit
(rectangle, •)	Section sized unit
(rectangle, ••)	Small Platoon sized unit
(rectangle, •••)	Platoon sized unit
(rectangle, I)	Company sized unit
(rectangle, II)	Battalion sized unit
(rectangle, III)	Combat Regiment or Logistic Group sized unit

- - X - -	Boundary between two Brigades
- - X X - -	Boundary between two Divisions
- - X X X - -	Boundary between two Corps
- - X X X X - -	Boundary between two Armies
X (rectangle)	Brigade
X X (rectangle)	Division
X X X (rectangle)	Corps
X X X X (rectangle)	Army

(+) After a symbol means the unit is stronger than its size symbol and less than the next size up

(-) After a symbol means the unit is weaker than its size symbol and stronger than the next size down

COMMAND AND CONTROL SYMBOLS

(flag)	Headquarters
(circle on stem)	A Control Point
(large circle)	An Installation
X X (rectangle)	A Divisional Headquarters
II LOG (flag)	A Logistic Battalion Headquarters

(circle, 7 X ○)	Control Point 7th Armoured Brigade
(circle, 7 X LOG)	Logistic Control Point 7th Armoured Brigade
(Y in circle)	A Fuel Installation
~~	Forward Line of Own Troops
II LOG (dashed box)	Projected site for a Logistic Battalion Headquarters

UNIT TYPE SYMBOLS

(oval)	Armour
(dome)	Air Defence
(missile)	Missile
(engineer)	Engineer
(bridging)	Bridging
(helicopter)	Helicopter
(airborne)	Airborne
(airmobile)	Airmobile
(anchor)	Marine
(transport)	Transport
RR	Railway Operating
(medical)	Medical

(box)	Multi-Commodity Supply
(ammunition)	Ammunition
(Y)	Fuel
(rations)	Rations
(materiel)	Materiel
)—(	Maintenance
(postal)	Postal Courier
(labour)	Labour
(⊗)	Supply and Transport
(⊗)	Transport Helicopters
)—(	Aviation Repair Unit
•	Artillery

1.

What is This Thing Called Logistics?

'The more I have seen of war the more I realise how much it all depends upon administration and transportation (what our American friends call logistics). It takes little skill or imagination to see where you would like your army and when; it takes much knowledge and hard work to know where you can place your forces and whether you can maintain them there. A real knowledge of supply and movement factors must be the basis of every leader's plan; only then can he know how and when to take risks with these factors, and battles and wars are won by taking risks.'[1]

The Liberation of Kuwait 1991

Much of the success of the Coalition forces in the Liberation of Kuwait 1991 has been credited to the logistic skill of the allied nations involved. General H. Norman Schwarzkopf, the victorious commander, described the successful campaign as a 'logistician's war'. Television reporters showed clip after clip of the Coalition's might deploying in Saudi Arabia – 670,000 men from 28 nations – and their newspaper colleagues commented sagely on the number of soldiers, vehicles and the tonnages moved to support them. The 150,000 troops of the US VII and XVIII Corps moved 250 km across Saudi Arabia in complete secret. The US 82nd Airborne Division plunged 400 km across Iraq and was still supplied and supported. On a smaller scale, the some 35,000 strong British contingent needed over 1,100 flights, more than 120 ships and deployed about 50,000 tonnes of ammunition and some 7,000 large freight containers during the campaign. All the pundits commented on just what a logistic triumph the campaign had been. But there were some, politicians, civil servants and members of the press and public, to whom 'logistics' was a new word. There were others who used it without real understanding; some were military men.

The Lifeblood of War

In peace, logistics represents about a quarter of most armies' budgets. In conflict, logistics is the lifeblood of war and an understanding of just what it involves is vital to all those concerned with thinking or planning for operations. It is almost unknown to find a soldier who will not acknowledge the importance of logistics. Without the means to wage war, the men, equipment and supplies, and the ability to distribute and maintain them in action, numbers of tanks and helicopters are just that – mere numbers. It is logistics which moves armies to where they can fight. It is logistics which keeps weapon systems firing and maintained. Indeed, so important is logistics that it features as a principal factor in almost every soldier's appreciation of the task facing him, and in the plan that is finally made. Unfortunately, lip service is often all that is paid to logistics. Politicians, civil servants and generals are sometimes child-like; they prefer to have the bright shiny new toys of more tanks, rather than buy fewer tanks but have enough spares and the like to keep what they have bought going. Indicative is that most armies support their modern main battle tank fleet with a repair and recovery variant based on an older tank chassis, often too slow to keep up with the newer tanks it is to support. Generals would often rather have just one more tank than spend the $4m cost of the tank on 40 spare engines and gearboxes to support the rest.

The Importance of Logistics to Government Decision Makers

All too often in political and military discussions, logistics is the last subject to be addressed; if in the little time available it can be discussed at all. Yet, without logistics, plans cannot be supported and will fail. It is almost as if logistics should be the first thing to be discussed, and not the last. Certainly this would seem to be the case the higher one goes in the spectrum of military operations. For logistics governs just how many units can be moved to a theatre of operations, and maintained there subsequently. Within the theatre of operations, logistics governs the phasing of battle plans and often the selection of tactical objectives. All this leads to the conclusion that logistics, like war itself, is best not left to the generals. Logistics is not just the obvious supplies of war materiel that armies have on hand. It is also the ability of a national infrastructure and manufacturing base to support armed forces at war, the availability of national transportation means to ensure that those armed forces can be deployed, and the ability to resupply those forces when they have arrived. Consequently, logistics is important to all those who help to prepare, shape and formulate strategy, and thus should be understood by government decision-makers and those who would wish to comment on government decisions; politicians, civil servants and the media.

Definitions of Logistics

Military activity is usually described in terms of tactics and strategy; where tactics is the art of handling troops in battle and strategy is the art of conducting a military campaign. There are a wide range of military activities which lie outside these definitions, but are still essential for any war.

Essentially unglamorous, these activities are lumped together by most armies under the heading of 'Administration', or some such similar title. Essentially, the key activities of administration relate to the movement and maintenance of armed forces: Logistics. NATO defines logistics as the science of planning the movement and maintenance of forces. In essence, this means logistics is divided up into a number of functions; supply, transportation, medical services, the repair and recovery of equipment, and a number of smaller functions such as catering, post and labour services.

Principles Of Logistics

All armies delight in rendering, or distilling, their experience into principles. There is much talk of the principles of war, for example, and how such-and-such commander either obeyed them and won, or disobeyed them and lost. Similarly, armies have crystallised their logistic experience into principles of logistics. Each army's definition might differ in detail but the same salient points are reflected in all of them:

Foresight
Economy
Flexibility
Simplicity
Co-operation

Foresight

Of all the principles of logistics, foresight is perhaps the most obvious. But it is also the hardest to achieve. The logistician is not only faced with guessing what the enemy will do, but also has the difficulty of finding out what his own general wants to do; the passage of information between hard-pressed operational staffs to logisticians more interested in 96 hours hence is notoriously difficult.

> There must be a clear-cut, long-term relationship established between operational intentions and administrative resources. Successful administrative planning is dependent on anticipation of requirements.[2]

Sometimes there is some excuse for a lack of foresight. Who in Britain in the early part of 1982 would have thought that within months an expeditionary force would have been mounted to travel the thousands of kilometres to the South Atlantic to retake the Falkland Islands. Indeed, when the force was first loaded for this campaign, there was no real idea that it would ever have to fight. Consequently this, plus the political imperative to be seen to be doing something, meant that the force left harbour with units and equipment stowed 'willy-nilly'. It was not until the force anchored off Ascension Island in the mid-Atlantic that its task become clear enough for the units and equipment to be stowed for an assault beach-landing.

But, using this same campaign, there were examples of logistic foresight. It might not have appeared that the largely foot-mounted commando and para-chute infantry involved would need much fuel. But portable petroleum fabric tanks and cross-country fuel tankers were taken, and proved invaluable in supporting the helicopters which were the sole practicable means of moving swiftly over the peat bogs and stone runs of East Falkland Island. Imagine the difficulties the logistic officer concerned must have had when he tried to convince his operations staff that 4,000 additional jerricans were needed and that vital shipping space should be given up to them. Yet these cans proved vital to the resupply chain that fuelled the generators powering the large number of isolated air defence missile launchers defending the eventual landing site. Even more prescient was the officer who, noting that the commandos' arctic warfare BV 202s had a lower ground pressure than a man's foot, and thus might be able to tackle the boggy terrain of the Falkland Islands, argued and won the shipping space to take some of them to the South Atlantic. Again, these vehicles proved invaluable.

Economy

In military terms, economy does not just mean saving money. It also means the ability to do more with the same amount of logistic resources, whether by purchase or by use. Thus General Slim, commander of Britain's 14th Army in Burma during the Second World War, when faced with a shortage of para-chute silk for the vital air-dropped resupply of Wingate's long-range pene-tration Chindit force, introduced the use of locally produced jute as the fabric for parachutes. This probably saved money but, even more importantly, the transport that had to be used to bring in the silk, which was in short supply anyway, from outside the theatre of operations was freed to carry other things.

Similarly, the use of road transport to carry logistic supplies over long distances is inefficient compared to trains. The two-man crew of a locomotive pulling an ammunition train can move the same amount as a 600-vehicle transport regiment. Consequently, the Allies liberating Morocco, Algeria and Tunisia in 1943 brought their own locomotives with them.

Flexibility

A 19th Century German general is reputed to have said:

Of the three courses open to the enemy, the only certain thing is that he will choose the fourth.

The Anglo-Saxons' Murphy's Law (anything that can go wrong will go wrong) is especially applicable to war. Twice, the reserve theatre ammuni-tion stocks of the US forces in Vietnam were almost completely destroyed as a result of accidents.[3] In the Falkland Islands campaign, the Argentinians bombed the British commando brigade maintenance area and by pure chance, because it had not been their target, hit the only reserve ammunition that it had been possible to bring ashore. US ammunition packs pushed forward to the first US troops flown in to help defend South Korea against North Korean aggression in 1950 had ammunition for weapons withdrawn from service at the end of the Second World War.[4] The weather, too, can aid the enemy. The great storm in the Channel during the Allied June 1944 Normandy landings drastically affected logistic supply to the troops in the beach-head and constrained the future conduct of the campaign for as much as six months. Less well known, the 1990 early winter Bay of Biscay storms severely affected the resupply of Europe-based coalition forces already in Saudi Arabia, and the deployment of the equipment of reinforcing US and British formations on their way to that campaign.[5]

Perhaps the best example of logistic flexibility required in a campaign is given by the 1982 British Falkland Islands expedition. When the force sailed it was not loaded for an assault landing. It restowed for an assault landing at Ascension Island on its way south. On arrival, the plan was that there should be minimum stocks on shore and that logistic support for the force would remain on board ships which would act as 'floating' depots in San Carlos Water. When the force was ashore and moving out of its beach-head, resupply and casualty evacuation would be by the large Chinook helicopters carried by the *Atlantic Conveyor*, a large container vessel. Unfortunately, the *Atlantic Conveyor* was sunk and all but one of the Chinooks went to the bottom with her. The success of the Argentinian air attacks on the shipping in San Carlos Water was such that the concept of keeping the resupply ships as a floating depot had to be abandoned. Instead, these ships sailed away out of aircraft range during the hours of daylight and returned when night fell. The plan was that the ground force would tell the naval commander what was required and the ship or ships that carried those items would come steaming in. Unfortunately, communications problems, and the difficulty in identifying just what was carried by what ship, meant that often the wrong vessel arrived. This plan was abandoned and the force moved to try to stock a Brigade Maintenance Area on shore at San Carlos. Thus the logistic plan for the Falkland Island operation had to be changed significantly, at least four times. It is only with well-trained and practised regular logistic staffs and units that such flexibility can be shown. The United Kingdom was fortunate to have both for this campaign.

Simplicity

Simplicity is a military virtue. Plans for war have to be simple if they are to be carried out by soldiers when all hell is breaking out. This is equally true of logistic planning and operations. Logistic communications are normally over far greater distances, and carried out with far fewer communications assets, than those of the combat troops. Consequently, things can go wrong. A clear, simple logistic concept that is in the minds of all those involved means that, when communications fail and other things go awry, individual staff officers

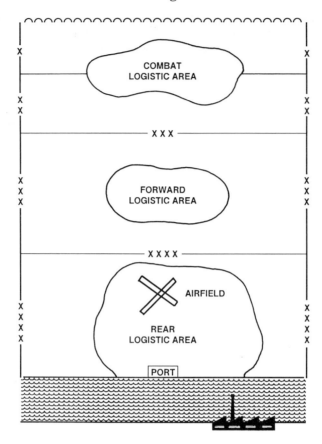

FIG. 1.1 Field logistic groupings for operations

and logistic unit commanders can take decisions in line with the general
thrust of the logistic plan.

The Duke of Wellington said of his Peninsular War supply plans that he
constructed them of rope. If they went wrong, and snapped, he would tie a
knot in them and continue. Complicated plans breed numerous logistic areas
and focal points. They soak up scarce logistic command and control assets and
demand extra managerial attention. Yet the essence of logistics is simplicity
itself. An army engaged on operations needs only three logistic groupings.

The first of these is the Rear Logistic Area. It is this area that serves as the
entry and exit point (or points) to the theatre of operations. It is in this area
that reinforcements of men and matériel disembark from their ships or
aircraft, are held in holding areas and are then moved forward to the combat
area as required. It is this area that holds theatre stocks of items to support
the formations further forward. It is in this area that the base depots,
workshops and hospitals so necessary to an army at war are sited. In 1950 in
Korea, the US Rear Logistic Area was the port of Pusan. In the liberation of

Kuwait 1991, the British Rear Logistic Area was the area around the port of Al Jubayl on the Arabian Gulf coast of Saudi Arabia.

The next logistic grouping is the Forward Logistic Area. It can be almost any distance from the Rear Logistic Area but a guide to its location is that it will normally be found between two things; the limit of the enemy's most effective depth fire long-range artillery and the railhead. A railhead is where the railway tracks end or it is unsafe to take trains any further. It is at the railhead that cargo trains are unloaded and their contents transhipped to vehicles. Thus it makes sense to site the holding areas for logistic stocks somewhere in the vicinity of the railhead; this saves on loading and unloading vehicles. In these holding areas will be placed the stocks to resupply the forward formations and those items of logistic resupply that are too valuable to hazard further forward and are only to be moved out of the Forward Logistic Area when they are desperately needed. One of the major tasks of the Forward Logistic Area is to form these mixed loads and to break up the remainder of the logistic resupply into formation packages. In the Liberation of Kuwait 1991 there was no railway leading from the port of Al Jubayl to the area of combat operations for the British forces. Consequently, an area near King Khalid Military City (about 300 km from Al Jubayl and 150 km from the Kuwait border and the Iraqi Forces) was chosen as the Forward Logistic Area for the British Forces. It had good civilian communications, it was a road centre, it had airstrips and a pipehead (the end of a pipeline) and was at the end of a very, very long drive from Al Jubayl, the Rear Logistic Area.

The last logistic area is the Combat Logistic Area. This is the area where the logistic stocks held are tied directly to the support of the combat units. The stocks will have arrived largely configured for safety and ease of railway transit and not in the loads of mixed ammunition and fuses that will be needed by units. It is safer, for example, to carry projectile warheads (the things that go bang when they hit the target) separate from the projectile charges (the things that send the projectile out of its launch tube and on its way to the target). The reason for this is that the charges, if accidentally set alight, just burn; they do not explode. So it is in the Combat Logistic Area ammunition and other loads are 'mixed' to the most useful form for the fighting troops. It is close to the fighting, but hopefully out of enemy field gun range, and ideally all logistic resupply items should be held on wheels. If logistic stocks are ground dumped the speed of combat action could well mean their being overrun and captured by the enemy. Consequently, the stocks held within the the Combat Logistic Area are a compromise between what commanders would wish to hold so far forward and the availability of sufficient vehicles to carry all this; plus the danger of presenting a massive soft target to enemy artillery and fighter ground attack aircraft.

Lines of Communication

There is really little change between Wellington's Peninsular 'Rope' along the Lines of Communication and modern day practice. The rope that is the

Lines of Communication is anchored in the national Base. It has the three knots that are the Rear, Forward and Combat Logistic Areas. Wellington's rope had only two strands, sea and road transport. The modern rope has two more, rail and air transport. The matériel of the rope changes the further one travels along it. At the Base it is almost all civilian. In the Combat Logistic Area it is completely military. Unlike Wellington's rope, the lines of Communication of today needs a military reinforcing steel core throughout its length if it is to be able to take the sudden strains of modern high intensity operations.

Co-operation

The benefits of co-operation are self-evident. There will always be a finite amount of logistic resources that can be allocated to units. Co-operation, between the formations of the same army, between the three different services of the same nation or between different nations, would clearly allow logistic resources to be maximised. All this is easy to say, but somewhat harder to achieve. It has been said that it is an unwise commander who allows his logistic sustainability to rest on the actions of others. Their priorities will not be his and support might be withdrawn at a particularly crucial time.

Alliances, to be sure, are good, but forces of one's own are still better.[6]

Wellington during the Napoleonic Peninsular War became particularly bitter about the logistic promises of the Spanish Junta; rarely honoured in full and often not at all. This highlights one of the problems of co-operation between nations. It is all too easy to promise logistic co-operation between nations in peace-time staff talks or command post exercises. But, often, the nation promising support is a poor one and, with the best will in the world, either does not have the promised resources or needs them for its own forces. Additionally, there is the problem of compatibility. Nations fire different types of shells and missiles and, although soldiers will gladly taste once the rations of an ally, the fact remains that they prefer to eat rations prepared in their own national manner and whose constituents are at least half-way familiar. Co-operation, unless one of the nations involved is to re-equip completely with the equipment of another, is therefore limited to fuel (most nations burn the same fuel in their vehicles and aircraft), transport assets and those few items of ammunition or matériel that are compatible.

There are, however, many examples of successful co-operation. Most of them involve the United States, ever a generous ally. Thus the UN forces (other than the British) in Korea were largely logistically supported by the United States; thereby allowing more of each national contingent to be fighting soldiers. Saudi Arabia was similarly generous to the Coalition forces fighting for the liberation of Kuwait in 1991, providing fuel and local resources. Within the Coalition, US aircraft flew British stocks from the UK and, inside Saudi Arabia, British tank transporters shifted US main battle tanks.

But What is a Logistician?

There is always a dichotomy between the operations and logistic staffs of armies. It is best explained by the following:

> Logisticians are a sad, embittered race of men, very much in demand in war, who sink resentfully into obscurity in peace. They deal only with facts but must work for men who merchant in theories. They emerge during war because war is very much fact. They disappear in peace, because in peace, war is mostly theory. The people who merchant in theories who employ logisticians in war and ignore them in peace, are generals. Logisticians hate generals.
>
> Generals are a happily blessed race who radiate confidence and power. They feed only on ambrosia and drink only nectar. In peace they stride confidently and can invade a world simply by sweeping their hands grandly over a map pointing their fingers decisively up terrain corridors, and blocking defiles and obstacles with the side of their hands. In war, they must stride more slowly because each general has a logistician riding on his back and he knows that, at any moment, the logistician may lean forward and whisper, 'No, you can't do that'. Generals fear logisticians in war, and in peace, generals try to forget logisticians.
>
> Romping along beside generals are strategists and tacticians. Strategists and tacticians do not know about logisticians until they grow up to be generals – which they normally do.
>
> Sometimes a logistician gets to be a general. In such case, he must associate with generals whom he hates. He has a retinue of strategists and tacticians whom he despises: and on his back is a logistician whom he fears. This is why logisticians who get stars also get ulcers and cannot eat their ambrosia.[7]

Most of the Great Captains of history have also been Great Logisticians.

2.

The Constituent Parts of Logistics

In modern warfare no success is possible unless military units are adequately supplied with fuel, ammunition and food and their weapons and equipment are maintained. Modern battle is characterised by resolute and dynamic actions and by abrupt changes in the situation which call for greater quantity of supplies than was the case during the Second World War. Hence the increasingly important role of logistic continuity aimed at supplying each soldier in good time with everything he needs for fulfilling his combat mission.[1]

Language

The profession of arms, like any other profession worth its protectionist salt, has a technical and esoteric language of its own. Langescheidt's dictionary of German military terms and expressions, for example, stretches to two very full volumes; yet serves only as a supplement to the main language dictionary. American and French military 'speak' are not much better. All of them, however, are better than the British military who, despite the rich and precise tool that is the English language, delight in the personal interpretation of terms that should be standard and universally accepted doctrine.

British staff college students bemuse their foreign fellow students for hours with debates about terms and expressions that their foreign colleagues might be forgiven for thinking should be standard and agreed British army doctrine. Things have not changed much since Wellington's time.[2] At first sight, logistics with its practical and pragmatic aspects and its relationship to speeds, capacities and distances might seem immune to this syndrome. Far from it. For, in NATO, 'Logistics is a National responsibility' and, to the complication of unagreed definitions (although great strides have been made in this area by the NATO staffs concerned), has to be added to the cacophony resulting from different languages. Conversely, and somewhat paradoxically, it is in the logistic field that NATO has secured some of its most telling and useful agreements; these range from the clearly necessary need to standardise on calibres of artillery ammunition to the not so obvious, but possibly equally battle-winning, decision to agree on a standard size for the common wooden transportation pallet, which would carry the ammunition and many more things besides.

Organisations

Language and doctrinal difficulties are compounded by the fact that none of the logistic services of the NATO allies are organised alike. Indeed, it is rare to find two logistic organisations that are the same; unless, that is, they share a similar historical background. Both the French and British armies' logistic systems are largely replicated in their offspring in the Third World and elsewhere.

Some logistic organisations, as in the US Army, have field logistic units through every level of command and group them into brigade-sized units if the numbers warrant it. The modern German Army, formed as it was to fight on its home territory only, has field logistic units only at the divisional and brigade levels. Its few field logistic units were largely resupplied from a matrix of multi-commodity static depots across Germany. Some other armies, either because they are too small to allow single Service based logistic services or because of deliberate policy, have tri-Service logistic organisations. In the French Army, for example, fuel is provided to all three armed services by the tri-Service *Le Service des Essence*.

Even when there is a seemingly obvious similarity, as between the US and British Ordnance Corps, there is none. In this case the US Ordnance Corps are repairers of vehicles, equipment and guns and derived their name from the guns they repaired. The British Ordnance Corps are the supply corps of the British Army and gained its name, in part, from the Board of Ordnance, the historical civilian department responsible for supplying all the British armed services. To muddy the waters even further, the British Ordnance Corps now just largely supplies the British Army.

Logistic Functions

It is sometimes difficult for logisticians to appreciate that logistics does not exist in its own right. It wins no wars on its own. Logistics exists to support combat forces. Its field organisation, in addition to history, also stems from what is to be supported, how the campaign is to be waged and at what rates, and how much money is available to finance the campaign. All this means nations organise their logistics differently. But most nations agree that the functions of logistics can be broken up into five main groupings:

Supply
Transportation and Movements
Maintenance and Repair
Medical
The Smaller Functions (Post, Catering and Labour)

Logistic Lines Of Support

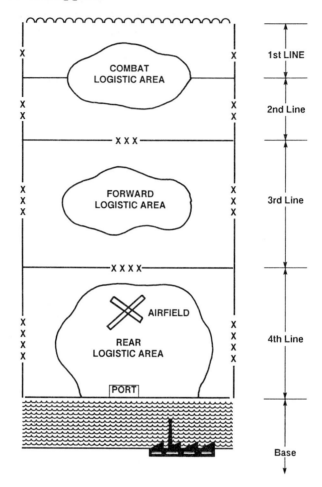

FIG. 2.1 Logistic lines of support

    Equally, there is general agreement that there are lines of logistic support
in which the type and sort of support varies as the distance from the combat
area grows. It could be argued that there are four lines of field logistic support
and the home-based military logistic installations and national industrial
base make up a fifth, static line, the Base:

    1st Line (Unit level)
    2nd Line (Brigade and Divisional level)
    3rd Line (Corps level)
    4th Line (Army level and, in NATO, national or in-Theatre static
    logistic installations)
    Base (Military strategic depots and national industrial base level)

Confusingly, these logistic lines of support do not run linearly from back to front, but run successively parallel to the Combat area and this is shown in Figure 2.1. They are all linked by the 'Lines of Communication' (sea, air, road and rail routes) that figure so prominently in scholarly works on war. 'Up' the Lines of Communication flow reinforcements and supplies. 'Down' them flow the casualties and empty supply vehicles and vessels and aircraft. Thus the Lines of Communication see a continuous two-way traffic.

1st Line

At 1st Line, the intimate support of units, the requirement is to give the unit what it needs, normally expressed in 'combat days' or 'units of fire', but no more. It replicates all the logistic functions but in a very small scale. Unless it were an artillery unit preparing to fire a fire mission, everything would be kept mounted in vehicles and the number of vehicles kept to a minimum. It is at this level that armoured ambulances and recovery and repair vehicles are found and, in some armies, even armoured resupply vehicles.

The British Army maxim for the siting of 1st Line logistic assets used to be that they should be kept out of range of enemy field artillery (the lighter and shorter-ranged artillery pieces used by every army as their general-use artillery) and only brought forward at night to carry out resupply. But, weapon ranges have increased since this maxim was coined and it is in this area, perhaps most of all, that the high intensity of modern conflict would be felt, and thus the requirement to move forward in daylight increased.

2nd Line

The British Army maxim for the siting of 2nd Line logistic units at the divisional level was that they should be sited out of range of the depth fire artillery (the long-range counter-bombardment heavy artillery) of the enemy. Weapon ranges have increased for these weapons as well and too far a withdrawal of 2nd Line logistic assets would prevent transport units from making a nightly return trip to and from the front line units. Indeed, ideally, any transport commander worth his salt would want to make more than just the one nightly trip and the consumption rates of modern high intensity conflict would demand this anyway. Consequently, at 2nd Line, assets and stocks are widely dispersed and most of the units truck-mounted, so that they may move to avoid an enemy penetration.

This line of logistic support holds reserve stocks for the division and houses the mobile general purpose workshops and the field ambulances of the medical service. It breaks down the ammunition, which hitherto has travelled as 'safe loads' into ready to fire packages suitable to be delivered directly to fighting troops. It would normally resupply forward at night, although the risky business of daylight resupply (the armour protective value of a general purpose truck or wheeled ambulance compared to the penetrating factor of a

30mm aircraft cannon or 155mm artillery shell is nil) can be attempted if the operational situation demands it.

3rd Line

3rd Line can be found in the back of the battle area, in what is called the Corps rear area. It transfers to vehicles or to the ground what has come up from 4th line by rail. It holds stocks of ammunition, fuel, matériel, equipment, vehicles and replacement personnel for the complete corps. This means large stocks have to be held and a vast area is needed. It houses the field hospitals, electronic and other workshops and other logistic units too vulnerable or vital to hazard further forward or more efficiently grouped and controlled at this level. It resupplies forward, normally at night and using roads, to 2nd Line, in the rear of the divisional area.

4th Line

Put simply, 4th Line is the disembarkation and deployment point for an army. If there is no geographical barrier (such as an ocean or a mountain range) this line of logistics is not needed in full and many items might travel from the Base strategic depots or manufacturers direct to 3rd Line. But if there is a geographical barrier then this level of logistic support becomes vital as a co-ordination and reserve holding point. It receives the input from the national infrastructure and the big strategic logistic installations. It can house the static depots, the base hospitals and huge tank workshops if needs be. It moves matériel, men and equipment along supply routes, customarily using trains, to the battle area. Various cost-cutting exercises have forced on most armies the 'One Base' concept for the peacetime resupply of forces stationed abroad. Unfortunately, forward in-theatre depots and logistic installations have been cut in favour of installations within the home country. Logistic support for US and British forces on the continent of Europe, each with a water obstacle between their country and mainland Europe, has been made more vulnerable by such cost-cutting.

Such a move, in time of peace, is perfectly reasonable. Unfortunately, the successful working of such a 'home-based' peacetime system is often used as an argument that 4th Line is not needed in war and that the embryonic war-only logistic resources that would have been devoted to it could be saved. Such cost-cutting measures are a triumph of will over reality for, while the 'One Base' concept should work in peace, it might not work in war.

The first problem is that, in peace, the lines of communication to the 'One Base' are open. There is no such guarantee in war; even keeping the Channel open for the resupply of the Allied armies in two world wars demanded Herculean efforts of the navies involved. Secondly, and one factor often forgotten in our modern age of high speed communications, the weather can severely slow the speed of sea-borne resupply. Thirdly, shipping is relatively easy to hire in time of peace, but not so easy to hire (what the British call

STUFT – Shipping Taken Up From Trade) in time of war. The Coalition forces deploying to Saudi Arabia discovered how much their own national merchant marines had withered since the years of the post-World War Two shipping surplus. They also discovered how difficult it was to find suitable vessels. Shipping has become very specialised and most vessels are much larger than their historical predecessors. This forces armies – and is rein-forced by their financiers' desire to economise on shipping – to load all their military 'eggs' in particularly large ships, the loss of which can drastically affect a campaign. The loss of the huge container ship *Atlantic Conveyor* in the British 1982 Falkland Islands campaign is just one example of this. A further shipping complication is that not all shipping companies or ship's masters are prepared to carry warlike stores; or at least will only do so at exorbitant rates. Fourthly, most modern shipping is huge and one shipload could need the best part of six transport regiments to move it away from the quayside. This number of transport regiments is unlikely to be immediately available in the rear area. So supplies have to be off-loaded from shipping and stored and guarded to await shipment further forward. This alone re-invents 4th Line and mocks those who would abolish it.

Field Logistic Concepts

Two main concepts for field logistic support dominate the debate about how land forces should be supplied. The first, primarily that selected by the Western powers, is of daily resupply. The second, largely that chosen by forces trained by the Eastern Bloc, is to tailor supply to the mission and resupply only after the mission is completed.

Essentially, these differing viewpoints derive from the available force levels and the likely tactics of the two sides. Perhaps the ideal solution, especially given their likely attacking mode, was the Red Army mission-oriented supply. The number of units and formations available to that army allowed it to fight a division with what it had and then, once its logistic supplies were exhausted, to put that division to one side and pass another, fresh and fully supplied, division through to continue the assault. The de-pleted division was then resupplied once the battle had moved on.

This option is not normally open to the West. First because the West just does not have the force levels neccessary to follow this type of logistic support: there are not enough divisions to go round and the withdrawal of one to resupply would create a dangerous gap in any defended line. Secondly, because the initiative traditionally lies with the attacker. Thus assaulting Red Army formations could afford the risk of a depleted unit which was vulnerable because it had to wait for resupply. Western armies can rarely afford this anxious period of vulnerability and had to attempt constantly to replenish their in-combat forces.

Much used to be spoken of the relative logistic strengths of the NATO and Warsaw Pact alliances. Pundits often took comfort in a comparison between the logistic strengths of a NATO division and its equivalent. It is true that

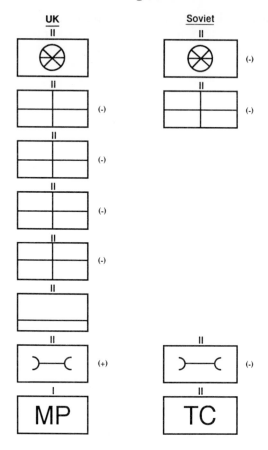

FIG. 2.2 Comparison of UK division and Soviet division logistic support

the NATO force looks much better off and much more likely to be able to sustain a period of combat when such as the comparison in Figure 2.2 is made.

But such an analysis was not completely true. Unlike the NATO forces, whose manoeuvre unit is largely the brigade, the Red Army's basic manoeuvre unit was the division. Reinforcing logistic units were kept at a higher level, held there in order to be allocated to the division achieving the greatest success. For the strength of Red Army logistic support to be fully appreciated, one needs to look to the logistic assets held at the 'Army' level (the Red Army equivalent of a NATO corps) shown in Figure 2.3.

It is at the Soviet 'Army' level that one finds some of the tanker, ammunition and transport battalions which were missing at the divisional level. Consequently, a truer comparison is to compare a NATO Corps with a Soviet 'Army' and on this comparison the Red Army formation looks as well off for logistic support as its NATO equivalent. Thus it is not that the Soviets do not have the logistic assets of their NATO counterparts, but that they hold them at a higher level.

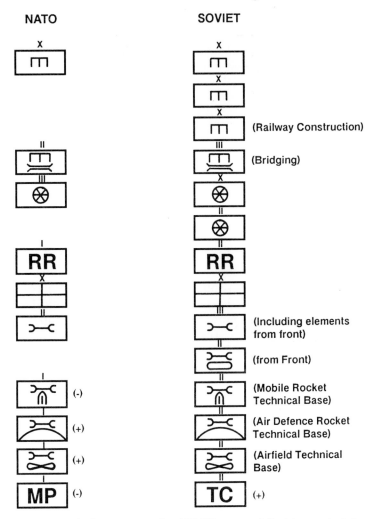

FIG. 2.3 Comparison of UK as an example of NATO corps and Soviet army logistic support

Furthermore, Red Army logistic doctrine, like its tactical doctrine, was to reinforce success. They regarded logistic assets, along with massed artillery, reserve formations, air power and intelligence, as a means by which a higher commander could influence the battle. Consequently, logistic assets were deployed to work where they were needed most, and not left idle supporting a formation which was not engaged heavily.

It would be wrong, too, to regard a Red Army formation's logistic support as stereotyped. Under their system, the mission of a particular unit, say to assault a strongly defended position, was examined and compared with prepared tables based on historical consumption rates modified by war-gaming and the application of 'military science' (a serious study for the Red Army General Staff). These tables, or 'Norms' as they are called, gave the required amounts of artillery shells and other natures of ammunition, expressed as 'Units of Fire'. It is these which are supplied to the assaulting unit and are delivered by Front or even Army level logistic assets.

The Red Army system did, and for its successors still does, have its flaws. Much depended on the ability of the Front and Army logistic assets to make their way through the clogged and congested combat area, competing for scarce road space with operational units moving to the front and surviving enemy air and long-range interdiction. Much, too, depended on the ability of Red Army commanders to read how the battle was going; for moving logistic support takes time. A Red Army commander had to decide where to reinforce, logistically, very early on in an action. There was an element of risk too. A depleted Red Army formation was particularly vulnerable to counter-action, because until it was resupplied its combat power was much reduced.

Lastly, the Red Army was not immune to the 'Bright Shiny Toy' syndrome that affects Western military men. The impressive listings of road tanker brigades and long lists of hospitals belied the fact that the equipment for these had never been bought; especially for reserve formations. Thus the Red Army planned to rely on requisitioned civilian vehicles and plant to equip the bulk of its logistic units. This had the effect of crippling the civilian industrial base from which all this equipment was removed. More importantly, when this procedure was followed for the Red Army invasion of Czechoslovakia, Bohemian and Slovakian roads were littered with requisitioned civilian vehicles that had broken down and for which, despite the almost military standardisation of Russian civilian vehicles, spares were not available.

Logistic Command And Control

If the difficulties of different languages and differing logistic doctrines and organisations were not enough to bedevil any putative logistician, the logistic assets of each nation, seem to be commanded and controlled differently. Most armies have staff organisation which are based historically on one of two models: that of the Prussian staff of Frederick the Great or that of Napoleon's French staff. Staff systems based on the Prussian model split responsibilities two ways, between a co-ordinating operations officer and a co-ordinating logistics and administration officer. The British Army adopted this system in the late 1800s and this is reflected in most of its offspring around the world. Systems based on the French model split the staff into five 'Bureaux' all reporting to one Chief of Staff. The First World War US Army followed the Napoleonic example, much improved it, and passed it on to its offspring around the world. By the time of the Second World War the German Army switched to something similar to the French system. Currently, NATO has agreed to standardise on five sections (G1 – Personnel, G2 – Intelligence, G3 – Operations, G4 – Logistics, G5 – Civil Affairs and Military Government) all reporting to one Chief of Staff. Ostensibly, the British Army also standardised on the NATO five sections. But it retained the one officer responsible for operations (called the Chief of Staff) and the other responsible for administration and logistics (called the Assistant Chief of Staff G1/G4/ G5). Thus the British Army's staff system is the only remaining staff which preserves the vestiges of the ancient Prussian system while supposedly being standardised along with its NATO allies!

The US logistic system (Figure 2.4) has logistic headquarters at brigade, divisional and corps level and these are commanded by professional logisticians. As the lessons of the liberation of Kuwait 1991 sink in, all armies are reappraising the way their logistic support should be provided. The US Army is good at such analysis and is looking particularly hard at the amount of logistic support provided at the combat unit level, 1st Line. It found that so much logistics was now at this level that combat manoeuvring was becoming constrained and is now considering the withdrawal of logistic assets from 1st to 2nd Line in an effort to reduce this restraint on combat commanders.

The French logistic system (see Figure 2.5) is similar to the American. While units may be provided by different services and their constituent parts may have differing establishments of men and vehicles, the overall organisation and methods of operation are very much the same.

The German Army is undergoing a radical change in its logistic structure. *Heeresstruktur 5*, the German army plan for its structure post-1994, recognises that the army will have to reduce and that, with the immediate Warsaw Pact threat gone, its earlier reliance on static permanent peacetime depots would not be enough to support mobile warfare. Consequently, the planned structure removes the few logistic units at the brigade level and concentrates all logistic assets at the divisional level. The static peacetime depots are now to be supplemented by a logistic brigade for each of the three planned corps.

The current British Army system (see Figure 2.7) is like none of these. At brigade level there is a five-man logistic element within the brigade headquarters but in peace time there is no controlling headquarters for the many brigade logistic units. Instead, for operations a 'Heath Robinsonish' Headquarters Brigade Administrative Area (HQ BAA) is cobbled together using bits of brigade headquarters and elements stolen from brigade units. The likely efficiency of this adhoc and somewhat amateurish grouping was always questionable, although typically British in its approach to the allocation of permanent and scarce resources to logistics. Worthy of note is that Brigadier Cordingly (commander of the British 7th Armoured Brigade in the 1991 liberation of Kuwait) on arrival in Saudi Arabia, ahead of the remainder of 1st British Armoured Division, discarded this concept. Instead he used a divisional ordnance battalion headquarters to command his brigade's rear area. This would seem to show that, although lip service had been paid over the years to the adhoc system for logistic command and control, 'thinking' British military commanders had realised its flaws. Fortunately, Brigadier Cordingly was able to use the ordnance battalion in this fashion because only a quarter of the peacetime British Army was engaged in the Gulf. Had the whole of that army been involved in the campaign, this unit would not have been available for the task and he would have had to rely on the adhoc system. This highlights the importance of ensuring that sufficient logistic

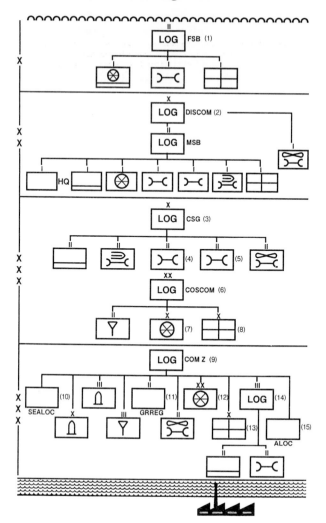

FIG. 2.4 The US Army logistic system

command and control assets exist in peace for, if they do not, there is no guarantee that they will be able to be produced in war; especially given the reductions that are being made by every army as part of the 'Peace Dividend'.

At divisional level the British do have a logistic headquarters (called Divisional Rear) but one which is rarely commanded by a professional logistician. Instead, the post is often used, in the best case, to acquaint a talented general staff officer with logistics (a subject about which, by inclination and temperament, a British general staff officer finds difficult to become enthused) or, in the worse case, to find a home for a general staff officer not needed elsewhere. In the Spanish Army, which is otherwise now refreshingly innovative and struggling masterfully with a small budget and the legacy of

Notes: Figure 2.4

1.   FSB - Forward Support Battalion. About 440 men and 250 vehicles. Often splits into two groupings for operating with the forward element (Forward Area Support Team - FAST)   commanded by the battalion support operations officer. This unit also commands the 1st Line Logistic assets of the brigade units.

2.   DISCOM - Divisional Support Command. This commands the large 1500 strong MSB (Main Suport Battalion) and the forward support battalions grouped with the brigades.

3.   CSG - Corps Support Group. Allocated on a scale of one per division within the corps concerned.

4.   General Support.

5.   Direct Support.

6.   COSCOM - Corps Support Command. Commands the Corps support groups as well as its integral units.

7.   Includes two 96 strong HET (Heavy Equipment Transporter) units for each division within the Corps.

8.   Includes two evacuation hospitals, one Mobile Army Surgical Hospital and one Corps Support Hospital for each division within the Corps.

9.   COM Z - Communications Zone.

10.   SEALOC - Sea Lines of Communication. A logistic control point.

11.   GRREG - Graves Registration.

12.   TRANSCOM - Transport Command.

13.   MEDCOM - Medical Command. Includes a general hospital, a field hospital and station hospitals.

14.   TASG - Theatre Army Suport Group.

15.   ALOC - Air Lines of Communication. A logistic control point.

---

the Franco years, this is taken to its extreme: while 40-year-old high-fliers might command armoured brigades as part of their deliberate policy of 'Rejuvenation', the colonel commanding an armoured division's logistic group (*Aggruppa Logistica*) could often be a 54-year-old ex-infantryman.

The Divisional Rear Headquarters is very much a staff planning headquarters. Consequently, each British Army armoured divisional commander seems to feel the need, rightly, for an executive headquarters to command his divisional rear area and to deploy and move the myriad of small, and some not so small, units found in the Divisional Administrative Area of an armoured division in combat. These units can range from air defence regiments to protect the field logistic installations, through battle casualty replacement units and prisoner-of-war cages to miniscule field cash offices and special prisoner-of-war interrogation teams. Again, the British Army system is to cobble together an adhoc grouping (called HQ Divisional Administrative Area) under the division's ordnance battalion commander. Interestingly, when 'push of pike came to shove' in the 1991 liberation of Kuwait, the British

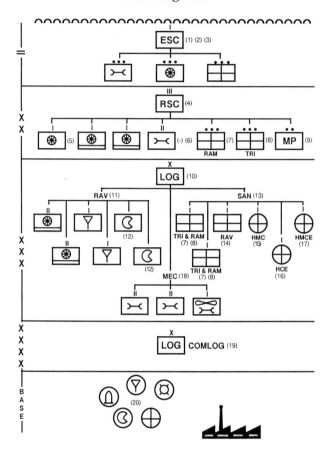

FIG. 2.5 The French Army logistique des annees 90 logistic system

found that the battle casualty replacement unit alone needed the resources of a full infantry battalion to command and control it.

Unfortunately, at British Army Corps level, the current situation is little better. There is a sizable logistic planning headquarters called 'Corps Rear'. But control within the corps rear area is wielded by reserve infantry brigades, whose commanders are forever looking towards how their brigades might join the main battle and who have little idea of the make-up or *modus operandi* of the myriad of specialised logistic units they might find in their areas and which they are supposed to defend. Alternatively, high-ranking logistic staff officers from Corps Rear can be tasked to command adhoc 'Sector Headquarters' with a temporary staff, begged/borrowed/stolen communications assets and a tactical responsibility for the area involved; as well as continued responsibility for the technical direction of logistic units of their functional concern. Again, the British Army's actual operational practice diverged from this. During the 1991 liberation of Kuwait, at the 3rd/4th Line logistic grouping at Al Jubayl, a logistic headquarters was set up under a

Notes to Figure 2.5

1. Escadron de Commandement et de Soutien = Command and Support company.

2. Not manned by logistic troops but by the troops of the regiment concerned.

3. The French Army does not have a brigade level of command. Divisions are smaller than those of other Western nations - nine major units as opposed to between 14 and 20. Resupply is achieved by the battalion level returning to the divisional 'Base Divisionnaire'.

4. Regiment de Commandement et Soutien = Command and Support regiment.

5. A 'circulation' or movement company.

6. In the French Army the maintenance function also supplies spare parts. Thus this unit also has a materiel stock holding function.

7. Section de Ramassage = Collecting Station.

8. Section de Triage = Treatment and Prioritisation Station.

9. Found by the Gendarmerie - France's regional police force but controlled by the French Ministry of Defence.

10. At the Corps d'Armee level the logistic brigade is formed on three logistic functional chains of command.

11. RAV = Ravitaillements. The resupply function, Ammunition, fuel, rations, water and clothing.

12. Manned by the 'Commisariat' and provides water and clothing as well as rations.

13. SAN = Sante. The medical function.

14. RAV = Compagnie Specialisee Ravitaillement Sante. A medical supply company.

15. HMC = Hospital Mobile de Compagne. A mobile field hospital.

16. HCE = Hospital Chirugical d' Evacuation. A surgical evacuation hospital.

17. HMCE = Hospital Medic-chirugical d' Evacuation.

18. MEC = Maintien En Condition. The repair and maintenance function.

19. COMLOG = Logistic Command. The French Army does not have logistics at the 'Army' level. Resupply of the corps d' armee comes direct from the depots and industry in metropolitan France. This resupply, however, has to be coordinated and the French Ministry of Defence deploys a brigadier commanded headquarters forward to the Army level to carry out this coordinating function.

20. Metropolitan France has a matrix of main and regional depots and military hospitals.

---

professional logistician.[3] This reinforces the impression that, while military planners might, in peacetime, decry the need for logistic command and control headquarters commanded by professional logisticians, in war they appreciate the need and are prepared to find the resources to man them.

There are even signs that these resources might be made available in peace time. The United Kingdom's 'Options for Change' exercise was underway when Saddam Hussein invaded Kuwait in 1990. The reorganisation of the British Army was put on hold until the campaign was over in order to be able to incorporate any lessons learned from the war. Not surprisingly, on the logistics front the British saw that they needed a logistics command and control system very similar to that of their major allies. A tentative system has been proposed (see Figure 2.8).

Like the Germans, the British have chosen to concentrate 2nd Line logistics at the divisional level. Unlike the Germans, and perhaps thereby revealing their prejudices against having logistic commanders, there is not to be a 'regiment' but two separate battalions; and nor is the corps level formation to

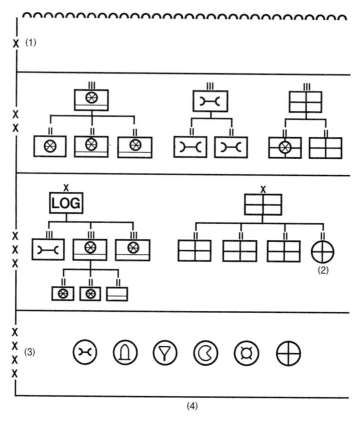

FIG. 2.6 The German Army heeresstruktur 5 logistic system

1. Heeresstruktur 5 has no organic Logistics at the brigade level. Logistics is centralised at divisional level and grouped with brigades according to task.
2. Between 4 and 8 static hospitals depending on the strength of the corps concerned.
3. Used to planning for a war on their own territory, the German Army has no 4th Line installations and supplies direct to the corps level Logistics and Medical Brigades from a matrix of regional depots and military hospitals.
4. The German Army had no need to differentiate between 4th Line and Base as it was to fight in its own country.

have the status of a brigade. Indeed, in a reducing British Army faced by demands to cut yet again the 'teeth-to-tail' ratio, it remains to be seen if such a system will be instituted or if the headquarters of the new system will be only on paper.

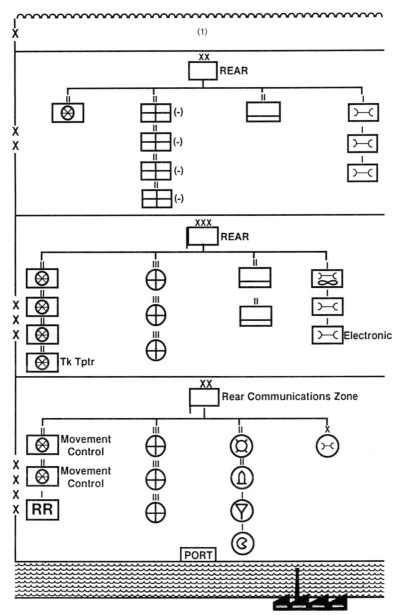

1. In the British Army, logistics is centralised at divisional level. Logistic units are grouped with a brigade for operations and would come under the command of the brigade headquarters.

FIG. 2.7 The British Army current logistic system

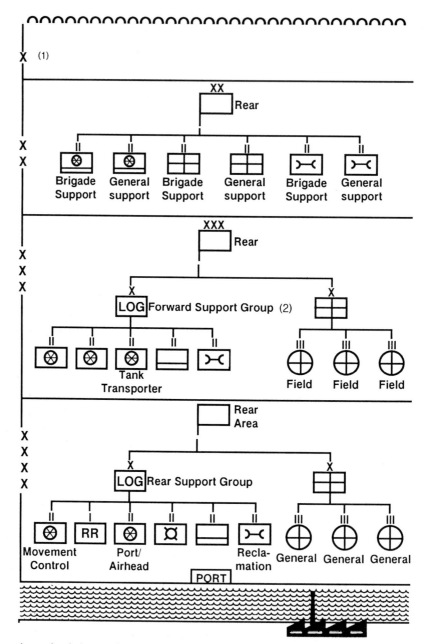

1.   Logistics continues to be centralised at divisional level.
2.   One Forward Support Group for each division in the corps concerned.

FIG. 2.8 A possible British Army future logistic system

3.

Logistic Support for High Intensity Operations

Logistic Planning Guidelines

Most armies have, at some time or other, been vulnerable to the accusation that they have prepared for the last war, rather than the next. Certainly, most calculations of consumption rates of ammunition and personnel and equipment casualty estimates are normally based on the experience of the last major conflict in which the nation concerned was involved. These can prove to be drastically wrong. The type of terrain over which the campaign is to be fought can affect logistic planning; but it is surprising just how constant most geographical logistic factors have been over the centuries. Logistic geographical planning errors are more likely to stem from a strange reluctance to accept the results of historical study as being in any way relevant. The hot desert water consumption rates of a Roman legionary, a British Second World War Desert Rat and a liberation of Kuwait US Armoured Cavalry trooper were all remarkably similar (20 litres per man per day).

More often, incorrect logistic preparation results from a misappreciation of the effect of a change of combat tactics. The success of the German infiltration tactics towards the end of the First World War meant that the advancing *Stosstruppen* rapidly outpaced their artillery support and rendered almost useless the massive stockpiles that had been built up in anticipation of the more traditional Western Front massive and lengthy preparatory bombardments. Incorrect logistic preparation can also happen when a new weapon system's effectiveness has been underestimated. During the 1991 liberation of Kuwait the 'Black Rain' of the Multi-Launcher Rocket System (MLRS) was very effective against Iraqi positions. The overall success of the Coalition air effort, the tactical surprise of the plans for the ground offensive and the Black Rain all combined to prove the Coalition's pre-conflict conventional ammunition consumption estimates to have been pessimistic by a substantial margin.

Nobody really knows what a modern high intensity conflict between two relatively balanced opponents might require in the way of logistic support. There are pointers. The Israeli/Arab conflicts, some specific US Vietnam operations and the 1991 liberation of Kuwait all give some indication of what might be needed. But all of these could be considered to have had special circumstances which, while not invalidating any logistic lessons, does mean that their applicability to a modern high intensity conflict between two relatively balanced opponents is questionable. Furthermore, weapons technology is moving at a remarkable pace and new weapons and equipment are constantly being introduced in response to the tactical lessons learned from earlier conflicts. These, too, will have their effect on logistic planning.

Until the early 1980s, most armies in NATO and elsewhere based their logistic reserves for war on the lessons learned from the Second World War modified by the experience of the Korean War. A 30 days' reserve of ammunition and equipment largely resulted. The lessons of the 1967 Arab–Israeli War showed, however, that modern warfare had changed. The consumption of specific types of ammunition had increased dramatically; particularly anti-tank and anti-aircraft missile rounds. Furthermore, the intensity of the conflict, although shortlived, seemed to show that the consumption rates for all logistic planning factors needed to be increased, from fuel through equipment to the men themselves.

All armies hastily studied their stockpiles and reserves. Similar methodologies were used and all of them had to reconcile two conflicting factors. The home side's weapons, equipment and unit effectiveness were easily worked out, albeit vulnerable to self-delusion and wishful thinking. However the effect of the opposing side's weapons, equipment and tactical effectiveness had also to be taken into account; for the home side's numbers on Day 7 of any future conflict would be certainly less than they were on Day 1. Furthermore, the effectiveness of the likely opposing side's weaponry and tactics was less easy to judge and estimate. Fortunately for the military brain, computers arrived to help in the figure work.

Battle Attrition Studies

Most armies started off by working out what losses they were likely to sustain before deployment on operations. These were relatively easy to work out because they could be based on peacetime breakdown rates of equipment. To these could be added the equipment breakdown losses likely to be experienced during the move out from barracks to battle positions. Interestingly, complex equipment like tanks, which are kept largely static in barracks for most of the year, suffer a prodigious failure rate during their first moves on leaving peacetime barracks. This should come as no surprise to car owners returning to their car after it has been laid up after any period of time. Nor does it come as a surprise to experienced armoured commanders, reliability experts and even theorists. The problem is that military equipment costs money to run and peacetime deployments from barracks are constrained by this. In the British Army, each tank or fighting vehicle is allocated a limited number of kilometres it can travel in a year and may go no further than this.

Then the equipment failures during operations would be calculated. Historically, this failure rate would be much less than that sustained during the first moves to combat positions; for both equipment and the men main-

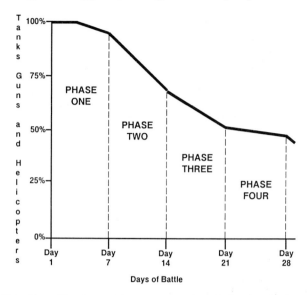

FIG. 3.1 The effect of battle attrition on an army's main battle winning equipment

taining it would have had time to settle down. Lastly there would be the battle losses due to enemy action to be added to the running total. The sum of this calculation would be taken away from the peacetime strength total of the army concerned and the resultant figure would show how much equipment might be needed to support that army at any stage in the likely future battle. (See Figure 3.1.)

Reviews of Ammunition Rates and Scales

If this were not complicated enough, most armies carried out a separate but complementary calculation of their types of weapon and how many rounds of ammunition they needed to fire from them. Into the equation were entered the types of unit and weapon, the target array it was expected to engage (how many targets it was expected to see and how concentrated, based on the likely enemy's tactics) and the number of rounds it was expected to fire in order to have the required destructive effect.

This latter figure was not easy to calculate. There is often a performance difference between 'trial' equipments, which are almost handmade from the finest materials and serviced by technicians who know them intimately, and the mass produced in-service model built from cheaper materials and serviced by ordinary mechanics. Manufacturers' and armies' estimates of the potential effectiveness of their weapons are rarely matched by the performance of those weapons on operations, and anyway, have to be balanced against the likely enemy equipment and tactics, both of which can be drastically over-or under-estimated. The German appreciation of the effectiveness of their Elefant tank destroyer in 1943 is an example of an over-appreciation.

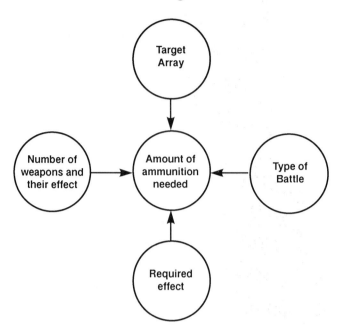

FIG. 3.2 Reviews of ammunition rates and scales

It had to be withdrawn from service after its first battles at Kursk, and never returned. The British pre-Second World War underappreciation of the effectiveness of the German 88mm anti-aircraft gun in the anti-tank role is an example of the contrary. Lastly in this equation, the likely losses to the equipment, both through breakdowns and enemy action, have to be calculated. The interplay of these factors is shown at Figure 3.2.

Stockpile Planning Guidelines

The merged results of these two equations gave the military a best guess for what they might need in the way of equipment, men and ammunition to fight a future high intensity conflict. But, when presented to the treasuries of the governments of the Western world, the reaction was one of shock. Not only were the new figures much larger than the result of previous calculations but, because they included so many highly expensive missile rounds, the cost of buying these reserves was prohibitive. Consequently armies, although aware of what they might need and that what they had was not enough, were forced to compromise and to plan for levels which were lower than seemed needed; but which at least could be bought.

Within NATO, the results of all this figure work were promulgated as the Stockpile Planning Guidelines (or SPG in the military shorthand). Each NATO nation has undertaken to implement these guidelines and build up their reserve stocks 'as resources allow'. Some nations, as one might expect, have been better able to find the money than others. Surprisingly, the best performers at this, amongst whom are the Dutch, are not normally those one would expect to score highly in any resource-dominated military league table. Conversely, it is often some of the richer nations that are most tardy in meeting the guidelines.

Types of Logistic Unit

The units to handle these new stockpiles are largely unchanged. Their organisations derive from what they do on operations and where and how that operational role is to be carried out.

Base Logistic Units

While all the logistic functions will be represented in the base area, the three largest will be supply, repair and the medical service in the form of its big base hospitals. The transport function will be represented but normally in skeleton form only for, this far back from the front, greater reliance can be made on existing civilian infrastructure; although history has shown this confidence can sometimes be misplaced.

Successive financial cutbacks have forced most armies to disband their large base military hospitals and rely on the civilian national health service. Similarly, the base depots and workshops have become largely civilian-manned and run. During periods of tension this can constrain operational flexibility unless money is made available; witness the fabled Swiss mercenary pikemen, 'no pay, no Swiss'. There are still bitter memories of the British Second World War London stevedores who went on strike for higher money when asked to load ships for the 1944 Normandy landings, and the industrial action throughout the United Kingdom when the British contribution to the Anglo-French 1956 Suez Canal operation was being mounted. Additionally, the civilian workforce is not likely to be a young one and is often capable of only a short – burst response to any crisis. All these base units are organised and equipped on civilian management lines with only a leavening of soldiery to provide command and control and a specialised military knowledge; as well as more often than not, taking care of the really dirty jobs experienced in any organisation.

Interestingly, while most of the Base installations are needed in peace and in war, some of the Base depots are not. There are really two types of depot. There are those that hold war reserves of ammunition, fuel and vehicles and which, once outloaded on transition to war, really just 'tick over', servicing the output of industry on its way to the front line. Unless the war is long and particularly intensive, these depots will be little used during hostilities. Then there are those like the material 'spare parts' depots whose work rates actually increase and continue at a high level once operations start and military equipment is used to its fullest. These depots will need a substantial reinforcement from the reserves to enable their high work rate to be maintained.

Field Logistic Units

Nowadays, armies' field logistic units are organised very much on traditional military lines with sections, platoons, companies and battalions. The size and composition of the logistic unit stems from the size and nature of the combat force to be supported and the tradition of the army concerned. As a generalisation, in the field and in other than supply and transportation, it is rare to find the logistic functions combined below company (100 men strong) level. The further back one moves from the area of combat, the more likely it is to find specialised companies grouped together under their own commanders. There are exceptions to this rule, typically the logistic support for lightly equipped formations or those with special roles like marine and parachute infantry brigades.

1st Line Field Logistic Units

At 1st Line, the combat unit level, all the logistic functions will be represented in at least section (eight men) strength; sometimes there will be more.

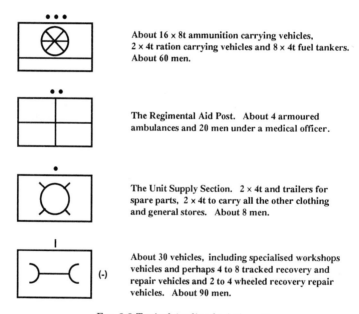

About 16 × 8t ammunition carrying vehicles, 2 × 4t ration carrying vehicles and 8 × 4t fuel tankers. About 60 men.

The Regimental Aid Post. About 4 armoured ambulances and 20 men under a medical officer.

The Unit Supply Section. 2 × 4t and trailers for spare parts, 2 × 4t to carry all the other clothing and general stores. About 8 men.

About 30 vehicles, including specialised workshops vehicles and perhaps 4 to 8 tracked recovery and repair vehicles and 2 to 4 wheeled recovery repair vehicles. About 90 men.

FIG. 3.3 Typical 1st line logistic units

Thus a British armoured infantry battalion will have a supply section, a large transport platoon, both manned by the men of the unit and a small repair and recovery company and a small medical platoon manned by specialists in those fields. (See Figure 3.3).

Brigade Level

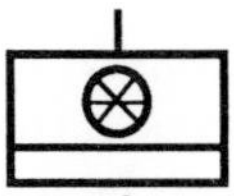

Around 72 × 8t general purpose task vehicles and 12 large fuel tankers. About 200 men.

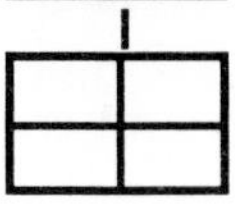

Around 12 armoured ambulances, 36 wheeled unarmoured ambulances plus a medical treatment facility.
About 200 men.

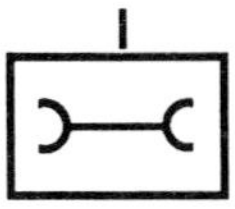

Between 10 to 20 tracked armoured repair and recovery vehicles. Specialist optronic radio and missile launcher repair vehicles. 4 to 8 wheeled recovery vehicles. About 150 men.

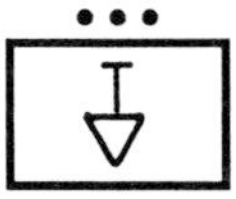

60 men for loading and unloading and preparation of unit loads.

A two vehicle, 6 to 8 man brigade post office.

Divisional Level

Around 200 × 10t general purpose task vehicles and 30 large fuel tankers. Can run static grounded stock sites, especially of fuel. About 800 men.

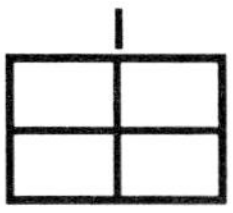

To support divisional troops only. No armoured ambulances but a big treatment facility to cater for the large number of divisional troops. About 200 men.

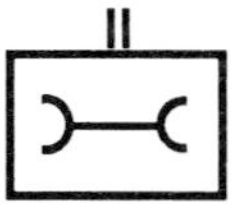

The main equipment repair shop of the division. 200 general and specialist repair vehicles. About 800 men.

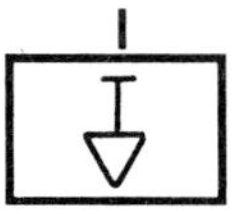

A general purpose labour and security company.

The divisional troops post office plus the couriers and their vehicles for classified mail. About 30 men and 15 vehicles.

FIG. 3.4 2nd line logistic units

2nd Line Field Force Logistic Units

At the brigade level, all the logistic functions would similarly be represented; again though, the detailed combination of these would be a result of the particular tradition of the army concerned and they could well be grouped with the brigade from divisional 2nd line for a particular operation or phase of the combat. One should expect to see at this level a repair and recovery company, a transport and supply company, a medical company and possibly platoons or sections from the smaller functions of postal and labour.

At divisional level, the remainder of 2nd Line, would be the parent battalions of these companies and further specialised companies of the logistic disciplines. Also here might be found very specialised elements brought forward from 3rd Line: helicopter repair detachments and air defence artillery repair groups are examples. In addition to supporting brigade units, divisional logistic units also have to supply the combat support units commanded at the divisional level, especially the artillery and engineers. It is these two combat support arms that require the lion's share of the available transport lift. Their requirements are so massive that their stocks can rarely all be held loaded on vehicles and some inevitably has to be ground-dumped.

3rd Line Field Logistic Units

At the corps level, the size of the task facing each of the logistic functions is so large as to justify the existence of major (battalion strength) units. There will be the major supply areas, each often holding up to a day's worth of all supply natures for the corps: the bulk of the corps' general transport assets (to deal with the off-load from trains and carriage to the corps supply areas or forward to the divisions) and the specialised transport units such as tank transporters, heavy engineer support vehicles and the fleets of wheeled ambulances and ambulance coaches. Here, too, will be the field (400 bed) and general (800 bed) hospitals providing major and specialised surgery and, importantly, the stability to be able to give sufficient post-operative nursing care. (See Figure 3.5.)

Interestingly, for the repair and recovery logistic function, there will be relatively few units at this line of logistic support. This function does not really follow the four lines of logistic support. Its task is to repair, and repairs are such that they can either be done quickly (at 1st or 2nd Line) or the equipment is so badly damaged that the repair is going to take a long time and the casualty needs to be taken right back to 4th Line or the Base and be overhauled in the base workshops. Consequently, while there will be repair and recovery units at 3rd Line, these will mostly be there for the support for the 3rd Line units themselves and not for any 3rd Line function *per se*. An exception to this stems from the growing complexity, especially in electronic components, of modern military equipment. The cost of the electronic repair with its test equipment and the special vehicle to carry it can be incredibly expensive (in the region of $3m) and the military 'Shiny Toy' syndrome can

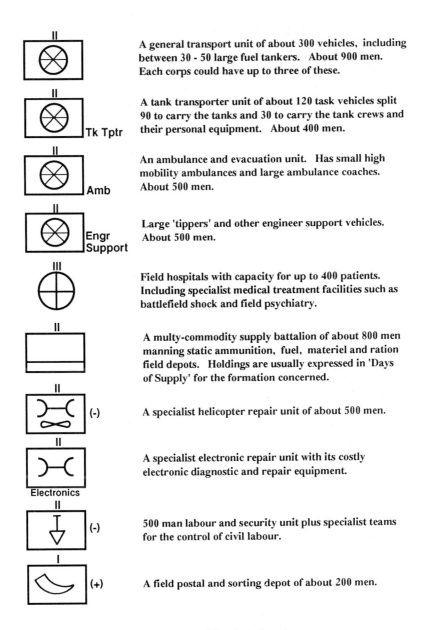

A general transport unit of about 300 vehicles, including between 30 - 50 large fuel tankers. About 900 men. Each corps could have up to three of these.

Tk Tptr A tank transporter unit of about 120 task vehicles split 90 to carry the tanks and 30 to carry the tank crews and their personal equipment. About 400 men.

Amb An ambulance and evacuation unit. Has small high mobility ambulances and large ambulance coaches. About 500 men.

Engr Support Large 'tippers' and other engineer support vehicles. About 500 men.

Field hospitals with capacity for up to 400 patients. Including specialist medical treatment facilities such as battlefield shock and field psychiatry.

A multy-commodity supply battalion of about 800 men manning static ammunition, fuel, materiel and ration field depots. Holdings are usually expressed in 'Days of Supply' for the formation concerned.

(-) A specialist helicopter repair unit of about 500 men.

Electronics A specialist electronic repair unit with its costly electronic diagnostic and repair equipment.

(-) 500 man labour and security unit plus specialist teams for the control of civil labour.

(+) A field postal and sorting depot of about 200 men.

FIG. 3.5 3rd line logistic units

also have an effect. Most armies do not have enough of these expensive equipments and keep them back at 3rd Line where they will be relatively safer than at 2nd Line, where they should be. Similarly, it is at this level that the expensive helicopter repair units will be found.

4th Line Field Logistic Units

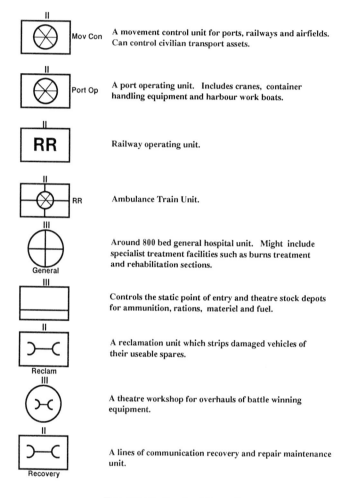

FIG. 3.6 4th line logistic units

The function of the 4th Line of an army at war is indistinguishable from those carried out in the Base. Thus at this level will be large static work-shops, huge hospitals and big supply depots. The logistic units that move in to run these installations will be organised on the basis that they will be using civilian buildings and other civilian infrastructure. They will, however, need to be organised on military lines and with their own equipment to supplement or complement that available from civilian sources. At this level of logistic support, such will be the size of the technical function to be carried out that the lowest functional unit will probably be the battalion. Taking supply as an example, this might mean that there is a brigade-sized supply group with petroleum, ammunition, and materiel battalions with perhaps a ration company attached. (See Figure 3.6.)

PLATE 1   A British Army supply convoy. Neatly tucked under natural cover and awaiting call forward. (*Author*)

PLATE 2   German Army recovery and repair vehicles and a *Leopard 1* Main Battle Tank. The *Leopard 1* has sunk into mud and, in trying to pull it out, the *Bergepanzer Standard* recovery vehicle has 'Bogged-in' as well. A second recovery vehicle has had to be called in to tow out both vehicles. Such incidents are the nightmare of recovery officers, and not just in the German Army! (*K. Zeisig*)

PLATE 3 A field ammunition storage site. The ammunition has not been sited tactically but has been brought together to show the amount of 155 mm shells needed by just one regiment of British artillery for one day of action. (*Author*)

PLATE 4 A British Army *Abbot* 105 mm self propelled gun having its barrel replaced. Such are the quantities of ammunition that modern armies expect their artillery pieces to fire that gun barrel replacement will be a common task as the internal rifling wears out. But spare gun barrels are rarely bought in the quantities needed. (*N.D.A. Seymour*)

PLATE 5 A main supply route of an army at war. In this case, the single main supply route used by the British contingent during the Liberation of Kuwait 1991. The vehicles are well spaced against air attack. This shot was taken at a time of light usage. More normally, this route was nose to tail with the logistic flow of an army at war. (*A. Taylor*)

PLATE 6 A German Army rail to road transhipment point. Rail remains one of the most efficient means of military transportation but the loads it carries are vulnerable to enemy air action and sabotage and, once battle is joined, it is likely that rail will be used only as far as 3rd Line. (*H.G. Ziegler*)

PLATE 7   A Base Ammunition Depot. The industry of most nations is incapable of reaching wartime production rates without a lengthy warning period and considerable stockpiling of raw materials. As a result, if money allows, armies produce ammunition in peace. This ammunition has to be stored in Base Ammunition Depots. Most armies have more than one because an accident, sabotage or air attack on a singleton could render an army useless. (*Author*)

PLATE 8   A Base Vehicle Depot. On mobilisation civilian industry might be able to produce load carrying wheeled vehicles for military purposes. Armoured fighting vehicles cannot be produced so swiftly and a wise army stockpiles this type of vehicle in peace. Any car owner knows that a vehicle left unattended for any length of time has trouble starting. Complex armoured vehicles have even more difficulty. Base Vehicle Depots are forever maintaining and test running their stock. (*Author*)

PLATE 9 A Base Repair Workshop. Modern armoured vehicles are very expensive. Where possible, armies upgrade those they have rather than buy new ones. Civilian contractors can be used, at a price, but workshops manned by the military can be used if no other useful work is available for them. (*Author*)

PLATE 10 A Base Materiel Depot. Such depots look like any other civilian warehousing facility. Whereas some storehouses might be filled with obviously warlike stores, others will be filled with less obvious stores without which an army might grind to a halt. (*Author*)

PLATE 11   The assembled vehicles of a modern armoured division. In this case the vehicles of the
British 1st Armoured Division at the port of Al Jubayl in Saudi Arabia awaiting repatriation after
the Liberation of Kuwait 1991. The sheer number of vehicles (over 9,000 vehicles and trailers) for just
one division of two brigades gives some feel for the huge supply requirement in modern war.
(*M.E. Wood*)

PLATE 12   The 'bits and pieces' that go to make up a modern rifle. In this case the British SA 80. If to these items are added the bits and pieces for radios, generators, vehicles and helicopters, and the batteries and cables to support them, the increase in armies' spare parts inventories over the last 60 years is explained. (*Author*)

PLATE 13   Rough Terrain Container Handling Equipment. All types of supplies now come in containers and their swift handling is crucial to the resupply of an army at war. Understandably, given the loads they have to carry and the rough terrain they have to cross, such equipments are expensive. There is a natural reluctance to buy rough terrain container handling equipment when armies own mobile cranes which can handle the same weight or civilian port facilities exist. But most logisticians would give their right hands to have a couple of rough terrain container equipments in their order of battle because of the speed with which they can move containers about. (*A. Taylor*)

PLATE 14   A Field Ammunition Repair Line. Mortar and artillery rounds are not the simple impact ignited high explosive munitions they were. A modern round can have proximity, delay, impact or vertical fusing or might be the carrier of a number of sub-munitions. Ensuring that mortar and gun positions have the right quantity and type of fuses is almost as difficult a task as getting the shells to the right place. (*A. Taylor*)

PLATE 15   Loading a container vessel. The civilian transportation industry's container 'revolution' has forced armies to adopt this means of transportation for movement from the Base right through to 3rd Line. (*M.E. Wood*)

4.

Supply

'Without supplies no army is brave.'[1]

The fact that no two armies seem alike is reinforced when one examines who supplies what and to whom. Again, armies supply systems stem from their historical background. Being very much traditional animals, armies resist change perhaps even more than any equivalent large civilian organisation. Yet supplying an army is big business indeed. The complexity and specialised nature of modern weapons requires a spare parts empire larger than most motor or electrical manufacturers. The cost of a pod for a Multi-Launcher Rocket System is $80,000 and even a relatively 'dumb' 155mm high explosive artillery round costs $2,000. This means any stockpile reflects a considerable national financial investment and needs expensive warehouses to ensure it is kept safely and does not deteriorate in store.

Most armies started off with the artillery supplying its own ammunition and cannon and, because this was the bulk of the ammunition being moved, also supplying the infantry and cavalry. Similarly, the engineers of most armies found themselves storing their own bridging equipment and supplying themselves, and the rest of their army, with mines and explosives and defence stores such as barbed wire and the like. As an army's medical service became established, it too found itself providing stores to the rest of the army.

While armies were relatively small and unsophisticated, such solutions to the supply problem were reasonable and pragmatic. But as such armies grew larger the result was a confusing blur as to sources of supply, an overlap in who held what (both the medical service and the supply service could hold folding stretchers) and a plethora of small depots all holding similar items. This was inefficient, both operationally and financially.

By the end of the First World War most armies had gripped the problem and had started to concentrate supply with one particular 'supply' service. This process is still going on. The Spanish Army in the early 1980s still had its artillery ammunition supply systems run by the artillery, tank ammunition supplied by the armoured corps and infantry ammunition supplied by the infantry. Even today, and although all other vehicles and equipments are supplied to the British Army by its Ordnance Corps, its Royal Engineers still store and provide engineer plant, vehicles and defence items to itself and to the rest of its army and the British Royal Armoured Corps is responsible for replacement tanks in the theatre of operations – but only then; earlier they are the responsibility of the Ordnance Corps!

One of the many NATO successes on the logistic standardisation front has been to get agreement on five classes, or generic types, of supply. Even so, the strongest of the NATO allies, the United States, groups its supplies into 10 types and it was these, and not the NATO five, that were used by the Coalition forces in the liberation of Kuwait 1991. If it was found necessary to use these 10 classes on operations it is likely that, peacetime NATO committies notwithstanding, they will be used again for future operations. However, for ease of comparison, the NATO classification of a type of supply is given after the 'Gulf' classification in Figure 4.1 and throughout this Chapter.

Class 1 Supply Items – Sustenance and Water

Armies have to eat and drink – Class I (NATO Class I). All have some sort of basic combat ration. Prepacked, often pre-cooked and needing only a little heat to be ready to eat, these rations are made up of what the nation concerned thinks should be the calorific intake of a combat soldier in action. Almost universally detested by the soldiers who have to eat them (the US liberation of Kuwait servicemen described their 'MREs' – Meals Ready to Eat – as 'Meals Rejected by the Ethiopians'), these rations can be eaten exclusively for only a relatively short period before both boredom and medical problems ensue and morale starts to drop. Variety in the menus provided is vital and committed chefs with just a few fresh items to supplement the issued combat ration can work wonders.

Some armies, notably those with a number of pre-planned and far ranging deployment options, also have geographically customised field ration packs. Peacetime exercises in Europe, taking place as they do within perhaps the most sophisticated and industrialised area of the world, have tended to draw attention away from the importance of Class 1 items. It is all too easy to supplement issued rations with items bought on the local market. But operations in a wartime Europe would be very different. Historically the fair distribution of food to the civilian population is the first government operation disrupted by the pressure of war, so this source of supply would not be available.

Operations elsewhere, where the infrastructure does not exist, or where there is a limited infrastructure but to use it would disadvantage the local population, require the import of great quantities of food, especially perishable fresh food. The handling of this food, and its subsequent distribution forward, requires a movement priority higher than most other supply items (which are rarely perishable) and specialised skills, handling and equipment such as refrigerated containers.

Bread is one of the invaluable supplements to the basic issued combat ration. Its relative importance reflects national characteristics; French troops regard its availability as particularly crucial. But, as a generalisation, its availability is important to the soldiers of all nations. Consequently,

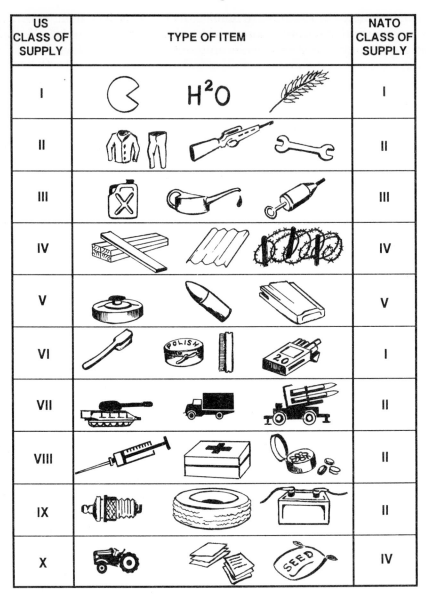

US CLASS OF SUPPLY	TYPE OF ITEM	NATO CLASS OF SUPPLY
I		I
II		II
III		III
IV		IV
V		V
VI		I
VII		II
VIII		II
IX		II
X		IV

FIG. 4.1 Liberation of Kuwait in ten classes of supply

Napoleon's mobile field bakeries are reflected in the orders of battle of almost every nation. Unfortunately, these field bakeries can rarely be afforded in peacetime (the British Army maintains only one in peace) and thus their wartime worth is rarely appreciated.

Class II Supply Items – Individual Clothing And Equipment

Having fed the soldier, the supplier must now clothe and equip him – Class II of Supply (NATO Class II). There are thousands of items to be considered, from the obvious basic uniform and personal load-carrying equipment to the not so obvious Nuclear, Biological and Chemical defence equipment and rifle-cleaning tools. All in all, some 200 individual items go to make up just the basic clothing and personal combat equipment for a soldier. This figure rockets in geographically extreme climates as even more specialised clothing and equipment is needed. Most of this clothing and equipment, especially if it relates to some military 'special' equipment, is not readily available on the civilian market. Thus contingency stocks have to be catalogued and stored.

Class III Supply Items – Petroleum, Oils And Lubricants

There has been an explosion in the demand for fuels and lubricants – Class III Supply Items (NATO Class III) – over the last 50 years. A Second World War soldier would hardly recognise current combat formations. The horse has disappeared completely and even the nominally 'infantry' formations of modern armies (based on their scales of available transport) would rate as at least 'mechanised', if not 'armoured', to the Second World War soldier. This explosion in transport has been exceeded by the often forgotten growth in mobile generators which, in addition to powering the lighting sets of units and headquarters, also provide the power for the air defence radars and launchers and the high-powered radio sets now available. Thus, during the 1982 Falklands War, one of the most crucial and battle-winning logistic resupply factors for the almost completely 'foot' British 3rd Commando Brigade was the supply of petroleum to its land-based air defence generators.

There has been, too, an undoubted fuel trade-off to the increased weight, mobility and speed of modern combat vehicles. The late 1940s British petroleum-powered Centurion tank would do 0.27km to the litre (0.5 miles to the gallon) while the 1960s diesel (a more efficient fuel) powered Chieftain could only manage just a little more, 0.44km to the litre (0.8 miles to the gallon). The advance in technology might have led one to expect a much greater fuel efficiency in the later engine. The more modern diesel engines are much more efficient than their petrol forebears, but they are also expected to do much more work. The Chieftain tank weighs about 60 tonnes, twice the weight of the Centurion. The marvel is not that modern tank engines are only slightly more fuel-efficient than their predecessors, but that they are better at all. The very latest generation of main battle tanks (like the Soviet T80 and the US M1 A1) are powered by turbine engines which are 'gas guzzlers' in the extreme and use more fuel than even the ancient Centurion.

The combined result of all these factors has been an explosion in the requirement for fuel for modern armies. The unbiquitous 'jerrycan' has been almost supplanted as the necessary fuel tonnages have forced armies to adopt bulk refuelling. Nowadays, the very vulnerable bulk fuel tankers have to be taken forward, right to the front line. As a result, a crucial part of each armoured squadron or mechanised infantry company's establishment is now its cross-country bulk fuel tankers. Unfortunately, even all-wheeled-drive bulk fuel tankers cannot keep up with tanks and mechanised infantry combat vehicles over rough terrain and this hampers operational movement and planning. Indeed, the jerrycan is making something of a comeback. Tactical commanders prefer it. It means that sub-units can refuel when they want, rather than when a bulk fuel tanker can be made available. At night, armoured commanders prefer relatively 'silent' refuelling by jerrycan to the noise of a bulk tanker's vehicle and pump engines.

Class IV Supply Items – Field Fortifications And Supplies

There has been less of an explosion in the requirement for field fortification items – Class IV Supply Items (NATO Class IV) – than in some other supply commodities. These items are some of the bulkiest and heaviest that have to be carried by an army at war. But there has still been an increase in requirement. The power, range and destructive capability of modern artillery is such that the reaction of every combat unit, even more than before, is to dig-in at every halt. Overhead cover is now vital, especially against air-delivered munitions, and while a simple rifle trench is relatively easy for an infantryman to dig, he needs defence stores to be able to construct his vital overhead cover and to wire his position. Consequently, front line infantry vehicles can be seen festooned with sheets of corrugated iron and rolls of barbed wire. In the divisional rear area there is normally a huge pile of defence stores held both as segregated packs for particular units and as a general reserve.

Class V Supply Items – Ammunition, Mines And Explosives

Ammunition, mines and explosives – Class V Supply Items (NATO Class V) – are perhaps the most obvious supply items for an army at war. Certainly, they comprise the bulk of the transport lift needed for a British armoured division in action at intensive rates of fire. In logistics, this simple fact of military life is one to which commanders and logisticians constantly return. It dominates tactical and logistic thinking and almost all other logistic problems pale into insignificance against the harsh reality of the figures. Less obvious than the transport lift problem are the hazards that munitions can meet before they are ever used in action.

The first of these is quality control. As much as 50 per cent of British shells used on the First World War Western Front during 1915 were 'duds'; they failed to explode when they hit the target. This was a result of a massive wartime increase in munitions manufacturing and the low tooling standards forced by the technology of the time. Additionally, the explosive standard of British shells was low. Until 1914 it had been German firms which provided the bulk of the chemicals for British industry. Today's conventional artillery rounds are much more complex, with variable, timed and proximity fuses, and the simple mine is simple no longer. There are double impulse mines (which wait for a tank's mine plough to go over before it explodes under the tank), off-route mines (which are command detonated; either mechanically, electrically or by radio control) and there are air-delivered mines (often timed to become inert after a certain period of time). Guided missiles have their warheads (optical, contact or proximity detonated), their guidance systems (radar, television, infra-red homing, laser or command wire) and their motors and propellants.

All these add up to a very costly and very intricate ammunition inventory for a modern army. In such complex munitions, the failure of one of the component parts can cause the failure of the whole. Not that failure of the warhead drastically affected the performance of the US Maverick TV guided missile during the Arab-Israeli wars. Originally designed as an anti-ship missile, its own weight and fuel load were enough to completely demolish any target it hit; the warhead was not really needed. This in turn prompted an Israeli restriction on their use. The Israelis had become accustomed to recovering and repairing enemy tanks damaged by other, relatively light, ground-based anti-tank missiles. A Maverick-struck tank was almost obliterated and could not be used again.

The ammunition quality control problem is complicated by availability factors. Simple munitions such as small arms and the simpler artillery rounds can be produced in the Third World and elsewhere. But production facilities for the more complicated shells and munitions are limited. This is changing as the Third World industrial base moves into higher technologies but, at the moment, the major powers have a near monopoly of the production of complex munitions. Even in the industrialised nations, the peacetime manufacturing base capable of producing such munitions is limited, and so is the ability to expand this base in time of war. Neither the US nor the UK were able to increase their ammunition production capacity significantly during the five months preparatory period prior to the liberation of Kuwait 1991, though NATO interoperability agreements did allow them to borrow or procure ammunition from NATO allies and elsewhere. With these additions their existing ground ammunition stockpiles had to be sufficient for that size of campaign; but, in fact, they were hardly needed because of the startling success of the sustained air campaign and a ground offensive that gave the Coalition the advantage of operational surprise against a demoralised enemy. The increasing lead time for more sophisticated munitions means that, should a protracted war be fought against a resilient opponent, the country or countries involved could be driven to something like the British

First World War 1915 gun rationing where some guns on the Western Front were reduced to just three rounds per day.

As a result, each army needs to hold massive ammunition reserve stocks, especially of complex and sophisticated natures, in depots, in peacetime. Most do not. The size and cost of these ammunition stockpiles means a strong political committment to the substance, and not just the surface, of defence. This does not happen often. Because the ammunition costs so much, and because it is almost irreplaceable, it needs looking after. Good husbandry of stocks and their constant inspection and maintenance is needed if this valuable asset is not to be found useless on the day of combat. This, too, costs money. The British Army, however, has found that the resources spent on good housekeeping and maintenance of ammunition stocks can actually save money. The testing of ammunition that is stored well, or 'Proofing' as it is known, often shows that the ammunition can be used for longer than its planned life. This means newer batches of the same stocks, and therefore more expensive, need not be bought.

If the possibility that the ammunition might not work was not enough, there is always the danger of accidents. Things that 'go bang in the night' have a habit of going off at other times of the day, and always when they are not wanted. The historical examples of sieges which succeeded because enemy action blew up the defenders' ammunition are legion. Less well known are the fortresses and positions lost because of ammunition accidents (Badajos in the Peninsula War for example). In modern times the US forces in Vietnam lost, at least once, the bulk of their reserve ammunition to accidental explosions.

Stocks are often held in bomb proof bunkers. Sufficient distance is left between the bunkers to prevent an explosion from one setting off another. Peacetime ammunition depots tend to be very big places. This dispersion is carried even further in the field. Bombproof bunkers are not available and there is always the danger of sabotage or, more likely, enemy air action. The 'footprint' (the area over which the individual sub munitions will spread) of a single modern air–delivered scatterable weapon is the area of a football pitch. Consequently, modern field ammunition sites are huge beasts; one of three in a British armoured division could stretch up to 10 sq. km.

Class VI Supply Items – Re-sale And Personal Items

The importance of the personal 'luxury' items – Class VI Supply Items (NATO Class I) – to a soldier's morale (although how a tin of boot polish ever got so classified has long bemused soldiers) is self-evident. Almost every army handles it differently. Very few provide nothing at all. Some make these items a regular issue which comes up the normal supply chain. Others, like the US forces, use the supply chain but charge the individual soldier for what he needs. British forces maintain their attitude to supply as 'trade' and embody civilian contractors as soldiers, sailors and airmen and have a hybrid system. Whatever system is used, this class of supply has diffuse but direct linkage with combat unit morale.

Class VII Supply Items – Major Equipments

The tanks, guns, vehicles and the other major equipments of the Class VII group of supply items (NATO Class II) are amongst the more obvious supplies needed by armies at war. However, because of the cost, there is a balance between what armies feel will be needed as reserve equipments and what their national treasuries can actually buy. Armies tend to be judged on their number of units (what is in the Shop Window) and not on the reserves which would keep those units going for long periods of sustained combat.

In all but the richest nations, or when an equipment changeover pro- gramme is underway, the holdings of reserve equipments are rarely as large as they should be. Or, if they are, the equipment inside the stockpiles tends to be obsolete or obsolescent. Sometimes this is not a bad thing. Reservists, who trained on the equipment when it was new, can be used to man it. Just because it is old does not make an equipment completely ineffective; better an older tank than none at all. But there are logistic implications in maintain- ing it (spare parts will be difficult or expensive to find and repair experience limited) and the operational implications (retraining a young regular tank crew in the middle of a battle on a completely different type of tank, or having tanks of differing ages, speeds and capabilities within the same unit) make this very much a second best, albeit cheap, path to operational sustainability.

Class VIII Supply Items – Medical and Dental

Some medical and dental supply items – Class VIII (NATO Class II) – are very specialised and can range from a complex mobile X-Ray machine to the provision of artificial joints and limbs. Particularly difficult to handle are drugs, for which uses other than medical exist. There is almost invariably a refrigeration requirement for drugs and other medical supplies and uninter- rupted refrigeration is surprisingly difficult to guarantee on the mobile battlefield. All too often generators break down. But most medical items are not so specialised and could come up the normal supply chain and be moni- tored by medical specialists along the way.

Perhaps the most difficult medical item to resupply is blood. Stored blood is remarkably short-lived (it has a shelf life of only six weeks) and, hitherto, military medics were the acknowledged experts on its storage and transpor- tation. In this area, as in so many others, medical research has made great strides and the provision of artificial blood is now a possibility.

Class IX Supply Items – Spare Parts

Spare parts – Class IX supply items (NATO Class II) – have become the lifeblood of modern mechanised armies. The reliability of modern equipments is slightly better than their predecessors, and the latest equipments promise to perform even better. They are, however, considerably more complex and the requirement to stock spare parts for them has increased by almost 300 per cent since the 1930s. Thus a British late-Second World War armoured division needed only one spare parts company. A current British armoured division has two small companies, and the elements of a third, and really needs all three.

Resupply of spare parts suffers almost from the same industrial base problems as the resupply of ammunition. Most military equipment, especially the big battle-winning equipments such as tanks, helicopters and artillery are what are called 'military specials' (equipment produced completely for, or so customised for, the military requirement as to be so). There are only a limited number of manufacturers, and they cannot stand still and, having produced the equipment, re-tool their production lines to prepare for the next order to be produced. Consequently, military suppliers have to guess what the spares requirement for an equipment is going to be and then buy-in sufficient spares to last for the time of the equipment in military service.

Such estimates are produced by collaboration between the suppliers and repairers, basing their estimates on the supplier's historical usage for similar equipments and the repairer's best professional guess as to what will be needed for the new one. Sometimes these estimates are wrong and the incorrect spares are stockpiled. Expensive contracts might have to be raised to get civilian manufacturers to re-tool to produce what is needed. But the biggest problem is not the new equipment. It is the tendency of armies to hoard equipment beyond its planned 'life'. All armies do this. In the short term it can save the high price of new equipment. But in the long term it costs more. Old equipment breaks down more often and uses more spares, which during the life of an equipment, ends up costing almost as much, and sometimes more, than buying new equipment in the first place. The British Army has in service a few armoured vehicles produced in the 1950s (the Centurion tank and the Saracen armoured personnel carrier and its other derivatives). In almost all nations, keeping such relatively ancient vehicles in service results from a hard-headed pragmatic decision to fund new equipment. It is cheaper in the short term to keep on the old than it is to buy new. This is well understood; but less understood is the huge managerial effort to keep them on the road. The more supply attention that is given to the few old types, the less can be given to the new types entering service. Although justifiable, it frustrates suppliers and has hidden costs in administrative, training and sometimes operational penalties.

The inadequate provision of spare parts, either because there are too few or because they are bought too infrequently, can lead to shortfalls, reduced equipment availability and frustration within combat units, suppliers and maintainers. Unfortunately, the purchase of spare parts is an annual event. It is not a major equipment programme and is an all too easy candidate for those in-year cost-cutting exercises that every army seems to have to face. It is sometimes said that this argument is simplistic. Financiers have to have some way to regulate the increasing costs of military spares. But the result is that spare parts become scarce, equipment availability drops off and soldiers' confidence in the reliability of their equipment is reduced. This can have a significant effect on morale. Once the financial strings are removed and, provided enough time exists for civilian industry to respond, the suppliers can move swiftly to at least reduce part of the problem.

In the early 1980s the British press questioned the reliability of the Challenger tank during its first years of service with the British Army of the Rhine in Germany. In many ways this was unfair. Most of the problems were due to the inevitable teething problems of any new tank. Neither the US M1 A1 nor the German Leopard 2 were immune to this and both littered the roads of Germany when they were first introduced. The main problem for all nations is that the spare parts which will be needed by new equipment are just not known. Only usage of the equipment shows which spare parts are needed. Rather than waste money on spares that might never be needed, armies frequently buy the bare minimum, knowing that if they buy more, the money could well be wasted. Once the spares usage of an equipment is known, it becomes a simple matter for the suppliers to gauge what spares they should buy. What they are able to buy depends on the money available. Governments do not have inexhaustible purses and, inevitably, there will be times of spares shortages. In peace time these can be alleviated by armies deciding which units and formations should have the priority for those spares that are available. In war, given enough time and money, much can be done. For the liberation of Kuwait 1991, the five months between the first deployments and the start of the war allowed all the Coalition partners some time for their industry to produce more. For some of the Coalition partners even this was not enough. There were reports in the British press and questions in the House of Commons alleging that a significant part of the British Army's tank fleet left behind in Germany had to be cannibalised in order to provide spares. However, that same press reported that Challenger's availability was excellent in the Gulf.

Class X Supply Items – Aid To Civilians

The military are often called to support disaster or famine relief in aid to the civil authorities, both at home and abroad. This requirement continues, indeed it may be even more likely, in time of war. The Class X (NATO Class IV) supply items cover all the previous nine and in addition include items not normally found in an army's inventory such as agricultural tractors. Use is being made here of an army's supply system, possibly the only working route open in time of disaster or war, to supply civilian or useful military items to a civilian population. As might be imagined, this is one of the most popular and rewarding tasks for any supplier to perform.

The 'Growth' of Supply Troops

One of the great lies of history is that modern times have seen a growth in the 'Tail-to-Teeth' ratio, especially amongst the suppliers. The real truth is

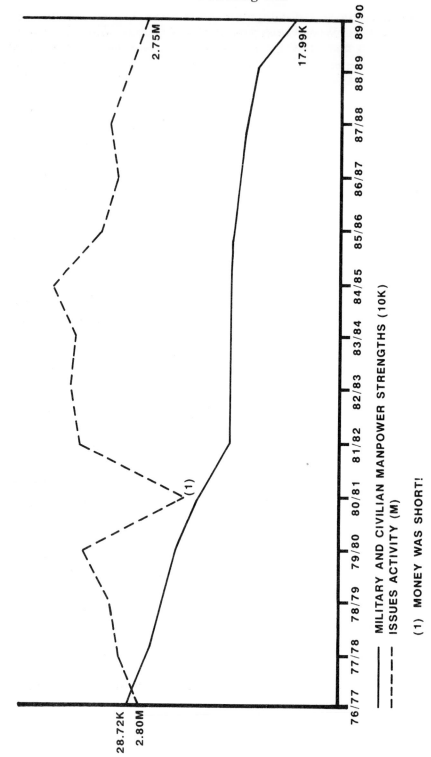

FIG. 4.2 Comparison of British Army supply manpower and issue activity

that the explosion has not taken place among the logisticians but has occurred in the combat arms themselves. A 1939 German Panzer division at full strength would field two battalions of tanks and two battalions of armoured personnel carriers (one infantry and one engineer) and the rest of its complement would be either on foot or horse-drawn. A present day division would field six tank battalions and six mechanised infantry combat vehicle battalions (for its armoured infantry) plus the equivalent of a further four battalions of armoured personnel carriers amongst its signallers and engineers. In addition, almost all the artillery of a modern armoured division will be armoured. The firepower, and therefore the ammunition consumption, of a modern division is some four times its Second World War equivalent. The introduction of just one new equipment causes a divisional spare parts company to in-scale at least 2,000 new types of spares. It would need at least two four tonne trucks and one 10-tonne truck to carry these spares. Thus, if the logistic manpower in support of such a growth was to have increased it would not be surprising. The contrary is the case. (See Figure 4.2.)

Two things have enabled the suppliers to handle the increased workload while at the same time keeping their numbers at their former level or less. They are the introduction of the computer and of mechanical handling equipment. Given these labour-saving devices, the suppliers have been able to keep pace with the huge increase in the number of supported equipments. With reducing armies everywhere it is clear that the suppliers will once again be asked to do more with less. Another two factors might help them: the introduction of bar coding and the introduction by most armies of demountable racks for cargo vehicles.

Bar coding is what every housewife sees on the side of the products bought in a supermarket. A simple pass with an electronic device over the code inputs information to a central computer. Its application to the military sphere is obvious. On the side of the ammunition loads or containers full of spare parts one pass would enable all the necessary information to be logged. Expensive and operationally vital items could be tracked every step of the way. Loading and off-loading procedures would be speeded and simplified. Most importantly, logistic resources will be scarce in any future conflict and bar coding and asset tracking could make the best use of those resources.

The demountable rack can be loaded or unloaded in just a few minutes and most Western armies are introducing them. They increase the productivity of transport units by as much as 60 per cent and, less obviously they will increase the productivity of supply units by perhaps a similar amount. Instead of concentrated frenetic activity in the dark to load a conventional vehicle cargo convoy, flat racks can be loaded during the day prior to the arrival of the transport, thereby doing more with less and in a much more operationally safe and effective manner. Given the introduction of these two measures it may be that, once again, the suppliers can show that they can do the same, or even more, with less.

5.

Transport and Movements

'Build no more fortresses, build railways'.[1]

Rail Movement

Perhaps the most efficient transportation method for armies at war is the train. Rail travel is particularly suitable for the carriage of casualties because there are less strains on the patient than on a bumpy road and most armies maintain ambulance trains. Rail transportation is especially important in the case of the bulk movement of ammunition – about 70 per cent of the total supplies that an army at war has to move. Ammunition is one of the heaviest supply items. Unlike other supplies, which bulk-out (fill a transport container with volume before they exceed its allowable-contents weight), ammunition can often weight-out (exceed the allowed weight to be carried before the container is actually filled). A standard military general purpose truck carrying ammunition will often weight-out before it bulks-out. This is not the case with a railway wagon and thus rail is a more efficient way of moving ammunition.

Rail has other advantages. Loading and unloading apart, to move hundreds of tons of supplies needs only the engine's crew. Consequently, trains are very efficient in terms of logistic manpower and vehicle resources. This was highlighted during the liberation of Kuwait 1991. The Coalition forces in Saudi Arabia found themselves operating in a theatre of operations which did not have the sophisticated rail network of Western Europe. They were expected to operate up to 700km from their ports of disembarkation. As a result, massive road convoys had to take the place of trains. In the case of the British, who eventually deployed only one understrength division, this took almost all of their army's transportation corps to find the men and the vehicles to make up these massive convoys.

Interestingly, the example of the 1868 British punitive expedition to Ethiopia was not followed. The 'Mad' Emperor Theodore II of Ethiopia had allegedly perpetuated various outrages on British nationals. General Napier's India-based punitive expeditionary force was faced with an inhospitable and backward terrain. The plan of campaign required an approach march of 800km (500 miles) followed by an assault on the hill fortress of Magdala. General Napier had some experience of this type of terrain and climate; he had taken part in the 1885 Sudan expedition. His solution to logistic support in such a backward country was to build a 40 mile light railway across the coastal plain to the start of the highlands. The railway was built in double quick time (three months) and poor Theodore and his followers were dispatched in a similar fashion. The Coalition had about the same distance to cover and no mountain barrier to restrict the railway's length to just 40 miles. The Saudi terrain was flat and the use of modern earth-moving and track-laying equipment would have meant that a considerable distance of track could have been laid in the four months or so preparation time. But no railway was built. The probability is that none was built because of a combination of a lack of trained railway troops and fashion; the military are prey to fashion as much as any other grouping and, in the automobile-dominated 20th Century, railways are just not fashionable.

Trains can be run as far forward in the combat area as the operational situation allows. The railway wagons themselves can be left 'stabled' (parked, still loaded) in a convenient siding until they are needed. All of which saves logistic manpower and vehicles. There are, however, some disadvantages to rail.

Unfortunately, the forward railway system of any nation at war is one of the first casualties of enemy action. It is vulnerable to sabotage, precision bombing with modern smart munitions or cruise missiles and offers obvious choke points to the enemy. The track and its bridges can be repaired; the 1944–45 German rail network proved remarkably resistant to damage and continued operating despite the Allies' overwhelming command of the air and continual destruction of its rolling stock and track. The loss of a train and its contents, compared to the loss of some of the vehicles from a road convoy, is disproportionately punitive to any resupply system. In modern warfare, a railway is particularly useful before combat begins, during deployment. Once hostilities start, while rail would be used as much as possible to move supplies as far forward as is safe, it is unlikely that the rail network to move them beyond 3rd Line would be open; or that it would be tactically wise to take trains further forward than this.

Secondly, supplies are loaded in railway wagons in the most efficient fashion, or in the case of ammunition, the safest fashion. This does not mean they have been loaded in the most useful manner for those who want to use the supplies at the other end. This is especially true in the case of ammunition. Units would like to receive their ammunition in what are known as 'fireable' loads – when the shell, its fuzes and the propellant to launch it would all be delivered together. But accident records show that to make a practice of moving combined ammunition in this fashion is an invitation to disaster. A simple railway wagon fire could ignite the propellant which would in turn 'cook' the shell so that it explodes. The explosion would in turn either fire other wagons or cause a sympathetic detonation – where the shock wave from an explosion causes simultaneous explosions in the shells and fuzes being carried elsewhere. As a result, ammunition is carried in the safest possible fashion, separated into its component parts. At some point it has to be off-loaded and reorganised into fireable loads. This off-loading normally takes place at 3rd (the corps) Line and the assembly of fireable loads at 2nd (division) Line.

Clearly, rail transport is a vital part of transportation for an army at war, especially for a modern 'Out of Area' operation, where the ability to deploy force quickly from the point of entry to the hinterland could mean the difference between deterrence and war. Consequently, it is rare to find an army that in some fashion does not try to maintain the skills involved in building the track and then operating the rolling stock over that track. But the investment of resources in such units is one of the first victims of any peacetime financial cuts that might be forced on the armies concerned. At best the function is relegated to the reserves. At worst it is cut so much as to be useless. The British Army maintains only company strength regular track-laying and rolling-stock operating units, and nowadays has hardly any reserves.

Wheeled Transport

The growth of wheeled transport in modern armies has been phenomenal. The 'weak' (two brigades only) British division deployed for the liberation of Kuwait 1991 had about 3,000 tracked vehicles and just under 10,000 wheeled vehicles and equipments. For the roughly 40,000-strong British force this meant that there was a wheeled vehicle for every four men and if the crews of tanks and armoured personnel carriers are removed from the calculation almost a wheeled vehicle for every two men.

This should not be so surprising. With the abandonment of the traditional reliance on railways there was bound to be an explosion in the wheeled vehicle requirement. Similarly, there should be no surprise at the two men for almost every vehicle. The most efficient use of a truck is not to keep it loaded and idle, but to off-load its contents and turn the truck around to go back and get another load. To keep a vehicle in constant use requires more than one driver, for a tired driver causes accidents and then he, the vehicle and its contents are lost. Two drivers as a minimum are required and most armies would want to work to a ratio of between 2.5:1 and 3:1 drivers per transport task vehicle.

Basic Military Wheeled Transport Types

Armies define wheeled vehicle mobility as 'low', 'medium' and 'high'. Low mobility vehicles are those restricted to road surfaces. Medium mobility implies some off-road movement. High mobility in a vehicle normally means all wheel drive and an equipment designed to operate across country. The workhorse of all armies' transport fleets is the general service truck. Normally capable of all wheel drive, to give limited cross country mobility, it can come in a variety of lift capacities of from 1–4 tonnes. This is the vehicle type found most often at the logistic 1st and 2nd Lines. But the requirement is always to do more with the same, or even less, and most armies now deploy forward medium mobility wheeled vehicles of 8–14 tonnes. Although these vehicles carry more than their smaller comrades, their mobility (and thus their ability to keep up with combat units) is often less, and their loss in action has a greater effect.

Further back from the front line, at the logistic 3rd (corps level) and 4th Line, cross-country mobility is not at such a premium and low mobility vehicles can be used. These are often just civilian vehicles painted green, bought off the shelf from civilian manufacturers to keep development costs down. Loads will be greater, from 14 to 20 tonnes, and there will be a widespread use of sizeable cargo trailers. These can carry up to 16 tonnes if towed by a loaded cargo vehicle or up to 35 tonnes if the prime mover is a tractor unit. Armies generally dislike the use of trailers, especially large ones, because they are so road-bound and so difficult to manoeuvre; albeit that modern closely-spaced axle trailers can partially overcome this. But the additional lift they provide forces their use wherever possible.

Specialised Wheeled Transport Vehicles

The growth of general transport vehicles within armies has been matched by a growth in the number of specialised variants. These range from engineer tippers and graders (civilian vehicles customised for the military) through ambulances (customarily based on general purpose vehicle types) and ambulance coaches to command and signal variants. But perhaps the two most important vehicle specialisations are the tank transporters and the bulk fuel carriers.

Moving tanks and other tracked vehicles for long distances along roads is very inefficient. The tank is not designed for such movement; it is designed to travel cross country. Under the continual pounding of the road surface its engines and gear boxes suffer and break down and its tracks break up. If its 'aggressive' tracks (tank tracks where the customary rubber pads are removed and bare metal is in contact with the road) are used, the road breaks up and becomes useless for all other users. The massive modern tank transporter solves this problem – 'Massive' because the weight of modern tanks and the weight of their contents when loaded for war means that modern tank transporters have to be capable of carrying around 70 tonnes.

The tank transporter has an operational value too. The speed of a loaded wheeled tank transporter is normally greater than that of a tank travelling on its tracks. Only the very latest models of tanks can match it, and normally at great cost to tank availability. Consequently, if rail is not available, tank transporters can be used to move a formation from one area of the front to another, often with the benefit of tactical, if not strategic, surprise. The Iraqi army achieved great successes during the Iran/Iraq war by lifting two complete armoured divisions on tank transporters and feeding them in at totally unexpected areas of the front. The British Army's tank transporter fleet can lift only about one large tank battalion; but then the British planned to use the Western Europe rail network and the Iraqi forces had no such option.

The growth of the transport fleets of the armies of the world have increased reliance on the bulk fuel road-tanker. Bulk fuel, apart from being dangerous, is notoriously difficult to transport cross-country. The changing centre of gravity of the fuel load makes any cross-country tanker inherently unstable. The fitting of baffles to restrict load surges can reduce the problem but most armies seem to have settled for a relatively small road-tanker about 4,000 litres for unit (1st Line/cross-country) purposes, and limited mobility civilian-derived tankers of about 10,000 to 15,000 litres at brigade and divisional (2nd Line). Further back at 3rd and 4th Line, straight civilian road tankers of between 20,000 to 30,000 litres are used.

The bulk fuel road tanker can quantitively supply modern armies' fuel requirements. There is, however, a problem of how that fuel is to be distributed. The modern tank's average fuel capacity differs between makes but is between 300 and 500 litres, but fuel efficiency is not all that good and they need refuelling just as often as their predecessors. Consequently, the problem is one of matching relatively low mobility fuel tankers to high mobility armoured fighting vehicles. All armies now deploy bulk fuel tankers far further forward than before and equip them with multiple dispensing hoses so that a number of armoured fighting vehicles can be filled at the same time. Some armies are even changing their tactics: their fighting vehicles now retire a considerable distance from the battle to refuel, which means time spent in action could be much reduced.

Sea Transportation

The provision of vessels, their manning and their convoying is the responsibility of each nation's navy and merchant marine; although it is surprising how many 'army' vessels armies seem to have. The British Army has a handy little fleet that includes at least two ocean-going vessels. The loading of ocean-going vessels should be of great interest to ground forces. Two basic options are open; to load tactically or not.

To load tactically means that vessels are loaded so that the equipment needed first is put into the hold last, thereby being at the top of the ship's hold when the hatches are opened at the port of arrival. Units, their equipment and logistic supplies are held on the same ship and vessel sailings are scheduled according to a desired order-of-arrival timetable. To do this presents problems. To load tactically is very inefficient in terms of using the available shipping space and could require up to three times the number of vessels. It is rare that an expeditionary force knows what all its constituent parts will be soon enough to influence the ideal loading plan. It is even rarer for the force to know what the operational situation will be in the theatre of operations when it arrives after a lengthy sea journey. The 1982 British Falkland Islands force had to put into Ascension Island to re-stow on its way from its hasty loading to the South Atlantic. Vessels, other than specialised military amphibious shipping, which can actually carry freight, equipment and dangerous cargo together are few and far between, although large civilian ferries can sometimes fit the bill. Consequently, valuable logistic assets can be concentrated in one ship, the loss of which could drastically affect the course of the subsequent campaign. The loss of all but one of the British 1982 Falkland Islands force's Chinook helicopters is but one example.

The alternative is to load non-tactically in the way which makes the most efficient use of the available shipping space. Invariably, this means a force's ammunition being carried in one ship, the personnel in another (or travelling by air) and its equipment in a third. The British Motor Brigade sent to defend Calais in 1940 discovered that its ammunition had been sent to Norway, where the formation had originally been destined. While it had its vehicles and heavy weapons, which turned up almost by accident after they had arrived, but fortunately before the Germans, the rest of its logistic support was either still in England or on the high seas to Norway. Not surprisingly, given the state of tank technology at that time, more of the Motor Brigade's tanks (about the same number as those available to their German opponents) were lost to mechanical breakdown than to enemy action. Within a few days, the tank battalion of the brigade was operationally non-effective.

The deployment of the UK force for the liberation of Kuwait in 1991 tried to avoid this and the first troops of the British ground contingent to deplane were repair mechanics from an armoured brigade workshop. Unfortunately, the desired order of arrival for the shipping had been organised for understandable presentational reasons. Visible signs of Western military might off-loading had to be seen as soon as possible so the first units to disembark at Al Jubayl were armoured. The bulk of the logistic troops and, more importantly, their vital mechanical handling equipment arrived at the same time or after the formations they were to support; this caused great congestion in the early days at the port.

The debate about tactical or non-tactical loading has been raging since man started to use the sea to deploy armies. The balance is between 'Speed of Reinforcement' and 'Speed of Movement'. With tactical loading the force arrives ready for operations – Speed of Reinforcement. With non-tactical loading – Speed of Movement – elements get to the objective quickly but are not fully operational until they are joined by the other elements of their force. Which is the right solution depends on the circumstances and luck.

Air Movement

Foot-slogging armies have a cynical doggerel which describes movement of ground troops by air:

If you've time to spare,
Then go by air.

Air travel is fast and covers great distances. This is true of the journey itself, but the preparation by ground troops for a flight is painstaking and exhaustive as their equipment has to be bound and secured tighter than any baby. The aircraft themselves are fragile and carry relatively little in the way of weight. From the soldiers' perpective, air travel is bedevilled by regulations (albeit understandable ones – the mercury of soldiers' compasses does unmentionable things to the control wires of modern aircraft) and breaks up unit organisations. Even the largest aircraft can only carry a weak battalion and in so doing separates the unit from its equipment and logistic support.

Armies try to avoid the pitfalls of air travel, while using its advantages in a number of ways. Some armies specifically tailor units and formations for travel by air. Their vehicles are configured to the size and shape of the aircraft that are to carry them. Light armoured vehicles are specially designed to keep their weight and size down, albeit normally at the expense of armour protection. Throughout the unit's equipment scales, efforts are made to save weight and to introduce the lightest possible thing that will do the job. But, at best, such units and formations are militarily very 'light' organisations and rarely suitable for high intensity conflict.

Helicopters

The helicopter may seem to be a panacea for most of a logistician's ills. It is not dependent on roads, can pin-point pick-up and deliver and is fast. Unfortunately, this is not always the case. Even the medium lift helicopters in service can only lift around eight tonnes. To get that eight tonnes loaded requires the logistic unit to prepare ('rig' as it is called) the loads for air travel. Once prepared, the loads have to be moved to the pick-up point by wheeled transport. It would be unwise to let a helicopter try to lift from a barnyard or typical wooded field ammunition site. All this would probably involve around 20 men for at least 40 minutes. Similar numbers and action would be required at the receiving end. To load an eight tonne truck needs just the truck's crew and one fork-lift driver and takes about five minutes. Of course, once loaded, a helicopter's speed far exceeds that of a truck. The benefit analysis is such that most armies would rather send a routine load by road unless the eventual destination was over 80km away.

The helicopter does, however, come into its own for a number of vital logistic functions. It is invaluable for the rapid evacuation of casualties and its use can, literally, be a life saver. It is similarly useful for the carriage of operationally vital items that are desperately needed forward, such as missiles (which are light in weight) and spare parts. Lastly, only the helicopter can easily supply a beach or bridge-head.

Demountable Loads

The tonnages that it is now estimated would be needed to supply a modern army in action are enormous. The conventional vehicles to carry them and the men to drive those vehicles would require at least a doubling of existing transport assets. But such a provision would be worthless, for the limited road network behind the front line would at worst be unable to take the traffic load, and operational movement would be hampered by massive traffic jams behind. At best it would provide the 'target rich environment' so beloved of fighter ground-attack aircraft or attack helicopters.

Most armies make use of civilian labour-saving transport techniques and have now standardised on the civilian International Standards Organisation's (ISO) 20 ft, 30 ft and 40 ft containers for the Base to 4th and 3rd Line general cargo movement task. This military 'standardisation' happened almost by stealth as armies used contractors for much of their Base and 4th Line peacetime transport and discovered that they would use nothing else. The civilian transport industry converted to ISO containers almost entirely by the early 1970s. Such a standardisation has proved a great boon to interoperability between armies, and means that armies now find it much easier to use civilian ports.

The military have, however, been slow to invest in container handling equipment, some more so than others. The weight of a fully loaded container can be very great and a piece of equipment to lift such a load and carry it across rough terrain will be very complex and expensive. The British deployed their whole fleet (three) of rough terrain container – handling equipment to Al Jubayl for the liberation of Kuwait in 1991. US forces for the same campaign deployed more than 50. The widespread use of containers has, however, caused one problem. When a military container is 'stuffed' (the delightful term used to describe the filling of a container) they fill it to the very brim. Some loads might fill a container but only use a very small fraction of the allowed lift capacity. More often than not, the tightly packed military loads of ammunition, spares or equipment puts a container at the very upper limits of its allowable weight. Military transporters are considering using half-height containers to get round this over-loading problem.

All armies are now introducing an invention which promises to revolutionise military transportation; moreover it is being introduced in an age of NATO standardisation and thus should be interoperable by those who have it.[2] This is the demountable 'flat-rack'. With this type of system, the military vehicle can lift its cargo bed, the 'flat-rack', off its back and lay it on the ground. The cargo bed can be loaded, with up to 15 tonnes in the British system, and then the vehicle returns and, in one easy go, pulls the flat-rack up on to its back and drives off.

It might be worthwhile to explain why such a simple invention is being regarded as having revolutionised military transportation. The basic transport sub-unit is a platoon of about 32 trucks. To unload or load a convoy of some 32 vehicles, at night, in the dark and rain of a typical wooded location, could take as long as two hours, depending on the number of fork lift trucks available. To put one of the demountable flat-racks on the back of a vehicle, or to drop it off, takes two minutes and a convoy of 32 such vehicles would take only 5–10 minutes to off-load or pick-up. Such systems do not reduce the supplier's time to load the flat-racks themselves; this still needs to be done. Now, however, it can be done smoothly and efficiently in between the arrival of convoys; or not at all if the load is to be moved forward unchanged. The productivity of the transport fleet is also enhanced. Whereas in one night of movement only one journey forward and back might be made[3] at least two, and sometimes three, could be attempted. Flat racks have other uses. They can carry light armoured vehicles, staff and radio containers, and fuel and water pods.

The British Army rushed its version of this type of system, DROPS (the Demountable Rack Off-loading and Pick-up System), into service in time for the 1991 liberation of Kuwait. Racks were produced to handle water and fuel in addition to the planned ammunition and general purpose variants, and the overall system, despite its operationally unproven nature and hurried introduction to service, proved invaluable in that campaign. Given the limited availability of rail in that theatre of operations, the British achievement would have been made much more difficult without the DROPS system.

Operational Transport Options

Historically the military transporter has been faced with four basic options for operating task vehicles over long distances. Rather like the US Army 'Red Ball Express' in 1944 France, vehicles can be run along a whole route, from loading point to destination and back again. But this is not liked by military men. Driver fatigue causes a greater number of accidents and it is difficult to ensure that vehicle maintenance is carried out at the right time. There is also the problem of who looks after a driver and his load if the vehicle breaks down along the route. It would take a very efficient command and control system to ensure that such strays were properly looked after.

An alternative is to run a vehicle from point of loading to destination and back again but to have the drivers change at posting points, rather like the Pony Express of the American Wild West. There are command and control difficulties with such a system; a driver could very easily become 'lost' to the system, as could the vehicle load. It is unlikely that the vehicles would be properly looked after by their temporary owners and vehicle availability would inevitably drop off.

Another method would be for drivers to exchange vehicles. This is particularly used at the 1st and 2nd Line interface, where full vehicles from the same unit might be exchanged for empty ones that had off-loaded at a combat unit. This works well when drivers are from the same unit and it can be guaranteed that the vehicle will be looked after and its maintenance carried out. It works less well when drivers from different units are involved. Almost always there are arguments over the state of the vehicles and, more importantly, sometimes confusion over the load: what it is and for whom.

The last method was not much favoured until the arrival of demountable rack systems. It involved a driver moving along only part of the route and handing over the load to another vehicle, which then took the cargo to its destination or another handover points. This method ensured that vehicles of the appropriate mobility could be used at the right lines of support. It also appealed to the 'tidy' military mind. It ensured that drivers stayed with their own vehicles and within reach of the control and support of their own units. Unfortunately, using this method with conventional rigid vehicles was very inefficient. At each stage vehicles had to be unloaded and loaded and this clearly wasted effort and time. But the arrival of the demountable systems has radically changed the way this method is viewed. The advantage of the demountable systems is that they can be unloaded and loaded in seconds and in doing so remove the principal objections to this 'Unit Stage' method. In the future, if a demountable system is used, this Unit Stage method seems likely to be the favoured way of operating military transport over a long distance.

Push And Pull Tactical Combat Distribution

Because the NATO allies had been contemplating a war where their formations had to be kept permanently in the line, NATO logisticians had to plan on resupplying those formations every day. Because the future battles looked like being of high intensity and the Warsaw Pact doctrine was to wage a 24-hour battle, resupply had to be a 24-hour business as well. History shows that battles never go as planned and many things can go wrong. In such circumstances the tactical distribution of supplies from 2nd to 1st line becomes a particularly difficult problem. To try to help simplify the difficulties, some NATO armies run a 'Push' resupply system, and others a 'Pull' system.

With a Push system the 2nd Line pushes supplies to the 1st Line combat units whether they have been requested or not. Of course what is pushed forward is based on likely consumption rates and some scientific modelling has gone on to decide exactly what is supplied; otherwise something that is needed will not be pushed forward. Such a system minimises the number of command and managerial decisions that have to be made and anything that simplifies war must be of benefit. Reports and returns, the bane of staff officers' lives and the things which dominate most logistic radio traffic, can be kept to a minimum for they need only deal with exceptions. Life is also made simpler further back because loads can be configured for certain units and this reduces the strain on combat units who would otherwise have to spend the time and effort sorting things out themselves.

But such a system has a capacity for in-built waste. The combat units might not have used up all their supplies of what is being delivered to them and overall consumption might be lower than planned. Because everything is automatic this can create bottle-necks at 2nd Line when the unwanted stocks returning from 1st Line meet the standard loads arriving from 3rd Line. As 2nd Line is a mobile line of logistic support this embarrassment of riches means some stocks might have to be left on the ground; which means they may become lost or abandoned to the enemy. Within the combat units there is a similar chance of waste. If the tank standard load includes a number of high explosive rounds, but the combat unit is to fight a delaying action with the priority targeting being enemy tanks, then the standard load will not include enough armour piercing rounds but will contain rounds that are not needed.

This is the dilemma with a Push system's standard loads; there is either too much or too little, but rarely enough.

A Pull system is much more efficient in logistic terms and because the only things that are delivered are those that have been requested there is little chance of waste. But a Pull system depends on effective and open communications to work and, on the battlefield, neither can be guaranteed. Moreover, the responsibility for getting their requests through rests with the combat units, who have more than enough to do in battle. Lastly, a Pull system inevitably means that there will be a delay between the logistic support being requested and its arriving at the combat unit.

Much depends on the tactical situation as to which method is adopted. Most NATO armies operate an amalgam of the two. For combat units, a Push system basic load is used which is based on the minimum likely resupply requirement; thus waste is avoided because what is delivered is almost certainly likely to be used. The transport commander keeps a loaded reserve ready to react to the Pull requests from those combat units for whom the Push minimum is not enough. The emphasis is shifted slightly the other way for the artillery. Their requirement stems from the fire plans they are to fire and, more importantly, from where those plans are to be fired; for this tells the transport commander where the artillery rounds are to be delivered. Thus the artillery work more to a Pull system than a Push.

The military transporter is crucial to warfare. Without an efficient distribution system an army will fail. There have been three 'ages' of transport: the age of the animal: the age of the railway: and the age of the internal combustion engine. It is a moot point whether the combination of the use of mechanical handling equipment and the demountable load systems mean that modern military transporters are entering a fourth.

6.

Repair and Recovery

The Growth of Maintenance Troops

Much has been made of the way that modern war seems to have brought an explosion of logistic troops. Some combat commanders wax nostalgic over 'the good old days' when they did not need to carry such a large logistic tail around the battlefield with them. Such nostalgia is unfair and unjust. As a generalisation, logistic units now find themselves supporting more with the same, or even with less. In one part of the logistic area there is a function which over the last 60 years or so has seen an explosion in its numbers. This is the repair and recovery function. The reason for this explosion is quite clear. A 1939 infantry division would have had only about 1,000 vehicles of all types and perhaps only 200 radio sets. There was hardly any other equipment worthy of the name. A modern armoured infantry division would have in the order of 3,000 armoured fighting vehicles and self-propelled guns and around 12,000 wheeled vehicles of various types. Within units, whereas the start of the Second World War saw radios issued down to only company level, now every infantry section has at least two: one for dismounted operations and one in the mechanised infantry fighting vehicle. There has been an even greater growth in the amount of complex electronic equipment issued to armies. If all this equipment were reliable it might not need repair; but it is not. Military equipment is often on the borderline of existing technology and the only sure thing about equipment on the borderline of technology is that it will break down. As a result, it is now customary to find that the repair and maintenance function of modern armies forms about 20 per cent of front line strengths.

Maintainability and Reliability

The 'Holy Grail' of the establishment writers of armies is to reduce this number. Rather like a 'Mantra', the magic words used as a reason for a proposed reduction in the number of 'maintainers' is that a new equipment will be more reliable than its predecessors. The potential cost saving as a result of better reliability is considerable. An equipment costing $2M to buy could cost 14 times that amount to maintain and repair it over its 15-year life. The cost of engineering such high reliability is great. Regular armies, with their high peacetime personnel costs, tend to favour high reliability.

Conscript armies, with their lesser peacetime manpower costs, logically should not be so keen on it. But their problem is one of training mechanics in the limited training time they have for conscripts. So conscript armies prefer high reliability as well; but are less pressured into carrying it to extremes. In the end, armies have to decide which route they will take: high reliability and high initial costs and a reduction in the number of maintainers, or lower reliability at a lower initial cost but with a larger number of maintainers.

Maintainers have, however, added to those two certainties of modern life, death and taxes, a third; new equipment will rarely live up to the reliability figures quoted by manufacturers to military men armed with cheque books. To be fair, there are underlying reasons for this. Military statements of requirement to manufacturers always ask for the new equipment to perform to much higher levels than its predecessor. Because of the tactical edge that technology can give a combat commander (Iraqi tanks in the liberation of Kuwait in 1991 were outclassed by Western tanks with their thermal imaging equipment that turned night, and smokescreens, into clear day), military manufacturers are always being asked to operate on the limits of current technology and beyond. Whatever the reasons, in the past, new equipment never seemed to need less repairers than before. Only with the very latest equipment does this cycle seem likely to be broken. At long last, the cost benefits of more reliable equipment are being fully appreciated and most modern equipment contracts have stringent reliability clauses.

The Warsaw Pact sought to avoid this conundrum by substituting numbers for quality, standardising on equipment types and making each new generation of equipment a progression from the old. The argument was that standardisation and simplicity enabled more to be built for the same price and 'simple' equipment could be better maintained by conscript tradesmen. But even the Warsaw Pact found that this aim was unachievable. While tank types such as the T80 might have had links with its predecessors, the technological leap between it and its predecessors was such that the two types types were, to all intents and purposes, different tanks. The Warsaw Pact, even more than NATO, followed a policy of not throwing away old equipment but handing it on to the reserves. Consequently, their maintainers had the daunting task of supporting in action equipment types for which spares and tools were desperately difficult to come by.

Vehicle Breakdown Rates

The contracts for new equipment all specify 'better reliability'; that is to say, more distance between breakdowns and need for repair than the equipment which is being replaced. The military 'buzz-word' for this is 'RAM-D': Reliability (how often the equipment breaks down), Availability (how quickly the equipment can be returned to service), Maintainability (how easy the equipment is to fix), Durability (how hard is the equipment to break). It has to be said that it appears that in some cases this is actually being delivered; especially in the case of automotive components. Despite this improvement it

Equipment type	A breakdown after ? Km
Older Tanks	20 Km
Newer Tanks	35 Km
Older Tracked Armoured Personnel Carriers	50 Km
Newer Armoured Personnel Carriers and Mechanised Infantry Combat Vehicles	100 Km
Other Armoured Vehicles	100 Km or more

FIG. 6.1 Armoured fighting vehicle breakdown rates

is still the case, especially on deployment out of barracks after a period of inactivity, that major military equipment breaks down. Failure rates depend on many factors which will be different for every army but, as a rule of thumb, there will be a major breakdown in a tank regiment or armoured infantry battalion every so many kilometres. (See Figure 6.1.)

1st Line Maintenance Units

Armies are forced to have repair and recovery vehicles with every company-sized combat group. These 'roadside repairmen' need to be backed up by a more substantial workshop to provide the repair facilities for optical, radio and other electronic repairs and specialist repairmen like metal-smiths. All these combat group repair assets are mounted in armoured vehicles, although the roadside repairmen tend to be mounted in older tracked vehicle types than those they support. Consequently, repair teams can have difficulty keeping up with the companies they support and, if there is a large gap between the ages of the two equipment types, sometimes the repair vehicle is incapable of carrying out some of the more complex repair tasks that might be needed.

The key priority for these 1st Line mechanics is to get their combat unit's vehicles back into action. Modern tanks are sophisticated pieces of engineering and just one little thing malfunctioning can reduce their combat effectiveness. Clearly, fighting vehicles will be got back into the battle sooner if the repair team moves to the vehicle casualty, rather than its being moved back to them. It will take longer to tow it back, repair it and then it still has to travel some distance back to the battle. As a rule of thumb, these roadside repair teams and their backup will only attempt repair tasks likely to last less than six hours. But much depends on the engineering of the equipment supported. A German Leopard 1 pack change (the removal of its engine and gearbox) could take as little as 30 minutes, whereas a similar operation on the older generation British Chieftain tank could take a full six hours if things went wrong.

2nd Line Maintenance Units

If the equipment is generally reliable and reasonably standardised, then armies normally centralise a back-up mobile workshop at the brigade level, with only a small repair platoon at the battalion level. If the equipment is not so standardised or not so reliable, armies are forced to have small companies with every combat unit and must supplement this with a large company-sized workshop at brigade level. But whatever the reliability of equipment, there will be repairs that will either take so long, are so specialised, or need expensive and sophisticated test and repair facilities, that they have to be done at 2nd Line.

2nd Line maintenance units have two distinct tasks. The first of these is to supplement the unit repair and recovery teams. It would be uneconomic to train every mechanic to repair all types of equipment; indeed, not every soldier would be able to master the brute force engineering of the automotive sections of tanks and the delicate electronics and circuit boards of radios and thermal imaging equipment. After all, these skills are almost separate disciplines. Thus the 2nd Line repair and recovery unit will have small teams of electronic and optronic specialists who go forward to a casualty when called by the repairers of a combat unit. Similarly, the 2nd Line unit would have a generous allocation of recovery vehicles. More often than not it would use these to supplement those at unit level. Often all the recovery vehicles of a formation could be placed under central control to support an obstacle crossing (where a broken-down vehicle on a bridge could stop an armoured force in its tracks) or to picket the route of a formation's approach march to battle so that unit recovery vehicles are left free to pick up their unit vehicles that break down during combat. Almost half a 2nd Line repair and recovery unit could be mounted in armoured vehicles, ready to be detached forward to help 1st Line combat units.

There are many repair and engineering tasks that will take longer than the guide-line six hours, where the unit mechanics do not have the equipment to repair the casualty or where the equipment is not important enough to take up 1st Line time and energy and can be left to 2nd Line to repair. These repairs are carried out by the repair group in the 2nd Line workshop. This is still vehicle-mounted, but on wheels rather than on tracks. They undertake repairs in greater depth, normally those which will not take longer than 24 hours to carry out, and it is at this level that the vital but expensive electronic and guided missile repair vehicles will be found. Once loaded with vehicle casualties that need repair, these workshops are difficult to move without abandoning the vehicles that need mending. In an effort to reduce the need for sudden movement and the abandonment of the vehicle casualties that could result, 2nd Line maintenance units are often sited somewhere near the rear boundary between the forward brigades and the divisional rear area.

There are some units whose equipment is particularly specialised, such as army aviation units and guided missile air defence artillery. These units will often be given a complete workshop of their own. Officially, but perhaps confusingly, they are said to have their 2nd Line support at 1st Line! Alternatively, these small specialised workshops can be brigaded together with obvious savings in command, control and administrative overheads; but it carries an equally obvious operational penalty: that support could take longer to get to equipment casualties. If the tracked carrier of these specialised weapons is the same there will be economies of scale and perhaps the specialised workshop need then only concentrate on the weapon system itself. Automotive repairs could be carried out by a general workshop. Among NATO countries the US Army has made the greatest strides in this area. Their 175mm (M 107) and 8 inch (M 110) self-propelled guns have the same chassis as their recovery vehicle (M 578). Similarly, their LANCE missile launcher, the LANCE carrier vehicle, the tracked artillery resupply vehicle (M548) and the HAWK anti-aircraft missile launcher all share the same chassis as their standard M 113 armoured personnel carrier. This custom is being continued with their newer equipments and the basic BRADLEY mechanised infantry combat vehicle chassis is also being used to carry the Multi-Launcher Rocket System.

When siting 2nd Line repair and recovery units it should not be forgotten that in some ways they are very akin to medical units in that, once filled with casualties, they are difficult to move. They can only really work effectively when static. As a move by them probably means the formation they support is moving, all their recovery vehicles could be needed to picket the route of that move. Thus the maintenance unit would have no spare recovery vehicles to drag vehicle casualties along with it when it moves. Maintenance units will tow as much as they can with them, and in so doing can double the length of their movement column and their movement timings, but with their heavy recovery vehicles gone, they will be unable to move all the vital main battle tank casualties. A maintenance commander has to weigh carefully the loading of his workshops and could well order one workshop to stay behind and to take in the repair work of the others, thus releasing these for movement.

3rd Line Maintenance Units

There will, however, be times when a repair cannot be carried out at 1st or 2nd Line, either because the equipment has been so damaged that the repair is impossible with the resources available to the forward troops, or because the nature of the repair is particularly specialised. In such cases, the defective assembly or 'Black Box' is removed and sent back for repair. If a vehicle is very badly damaged, or the supported force is withdrawing, it is dumped at a collecting point for recovery assets from 3rd Line (the corps level) to come forward and pick it up. This function is an unglamorous one but vital to what the military call 'force regeneration', that is the ability of military forces, after an action, to reorganise, to fill the gaps in its ranks and to declare itself ready for future operations.

In the Second World War Western Desert campaign the Germans were particularly keen and efficient at 'scavenging' the battlefield for wrecks, of the Allies as well as their own; they were forced to do so because of their slim and constantly interrupted Mediteranean lines of supply. The Germans were able to form complete transport regiments using allied vehicles, which did not help Allied pilots' 'Friend or Foe' recognition. Combat clashes resulted as the opposing sides squabbled over the same area of an ancient battlefield as they attempted to provide protection for scavenging repair teams. Perhaps the most effective army at this backloading of severe equipment casualties, and their turn-round back to the battle, are the Israelis. A severely battle-damaged tank can take less than 24 hours to be evacuated back to Israeli 3rd Line, completely refurbished and be pushed forward fully-manned and loaded for operations.

At 3rd Line there are relatively few repair and recovery assets. Apart from the reclamation units (which break down equipment damaged beyond repair for salvageable spare parts), perhaps some specialised battle-damage repair groups, the specialised electronic and aircraft repair units and the integral 1st Line support of the 3rd Line units themselves, there will be very little.

4th Line Maintenance Units

If a vehicle cannot be repaired at 1st or 2nd Line, the scale of the repair, the resources the repair will need and the time it would take to carry out are such that it probably warrants evacuation back to a 4th Line or Base workshop. 4th Line workshops might not exist in peace time but an army involved in a lengthy high intensity conflict should consider introducing them once hostilities start. The reason is based on sheer time and motion. If no 4th Line workshop existed the armoured casualty would have to be taken back to the home country and the Base workshops or civilian factory there; for it is very unlikely that there would be a suitable plant in the theatre of operations. If the liberation of Kuwait had caused this sort of vehicle casualty to a Western nation, it would have taken at least a month to get a tank back to a Base workshop, and a further month to return it to Saudi Arabia. A tank could have been out of the battle line two months longer than necessary. It is for this reason that the British forces facing the Axis Second World War Western Desert offensive created a vast workshop complex in the Suez Canal Zone.

It is at the 4th Line workshops, or the Base workshops if 4th Line workshops do not exist, that major equipments such as tanks can be completely stripped down and rebuilt. The limiting factor for such workshops used to be the lift capacity of the overhead cranes available. Cranes capable of lifting up to 20 tonnes are needed if the turrets of modern main battle tanks are to be lifted off their hulls, or 50 tons if the complete tank has to be lifted. But, nowadays, the introduction of advanced electronics into almost every type of military equipment has added the requirement for such workshops to have 'clean' rooms where the work area can be sealed off and the air filtered to remove all particles which might affect delicate electronics or optical components. Quite possibly these specialised facilities could be manned by workers from the civilian firms that built the equipment. But a military command, control and administration structure would be needed, both to direct the contractors and to provide an interface between the civilian and military systems.

The 'Black Box' Problem

Perhaps the biggest change that has happened to the repair function of modern armies has been the introduction of 'Black Boxes', so-called because the tank crewmen, and sometimes the repair technician, have little idea of what goes on inside them and is forbidden to open them anyway. Modern main battle tanks can now be fitted with image intensifying or thermal imaging equipment to enable targets to be seen at night or in bad weather. Their fire control systems are often computerised and the range to the target is found by using a laser. All this new equipment could not be fitted within a tank's turret without the miniaturisation possible from the introduction of micro-chip technology. This places the traditional grease-stained unit repair mechanic in something of a dilemma. Even if he could open up a malfunctioning Black Box, it is unlikely that he, in the forward area, would have either the knowledge or equipment to be able to put things right. Consequently, the Black Box has to be replaced; hence the more official military description of them as 'Line Replaceable Units'.

But this in turn causes two problems: which of the myriad of Black Boxes in the tank's turret is the one that is malfunctioning, and is there a replacement Black Box of this type available? The diagnostic problems facing the repair mechanic should not be underestimated; there will be many Black Boxes in just one function. Diagnostic kits can be as expensive as the equipment itself and there is always the possibility of an expensive diagnostic error. As a result, armies are now building into modern armoured fighting vehicles self-diagnosing kits that will tell the crew, and the repair mechanic, just which particular bit is malfunctioning.

But then the problem arises whether there is a replacement Black Box available. Such items will be expensive, liable to damage in transit, especially in the forward area, and until the replacement is found the main equipment concerned will be useless. Unfortunately, this is an area in which modern armies are loth to invest scarce resources and thus many of the fine modern fighting vehicles seen on television and newsreels probably have at least one major turret system that is not working, and a tank with a malfunctioning major turret system is a vulnerable tank.

While the individual price for modern army equipment is nowhere near the $30M paid for modern fighter aircraft or for the even more expensive modern naval vessel, armies need greater numbers than their naval and air force comrades. The sum of the numbers involved, plus the cost of in-built reliability and in-service maintenance, is becoming prohibitive for almost all armies. They have to decide if the RAM-D they are demanding is worth it. They have to decide if it is better to have an equipment that breaks down every 10 days and takes 10 hours to repair, compared to one that breaks down every 10 hours but takes only 10 minutes to repair. Built-in test equipment might mean that vehicle crewmen can replace the Black Boxes that would otherwise have needed a trained repairman. But this means the crewmen have to have faith in their test equipment, which is just as likely to mal-function as the Black Boxes.

With high technology and expensive equipment it becomes even more important that maintenance units should improve their productivity. They can only work when static. Yet the modern, more open, battlefield would seem to require them to move more often. The probability is that the future will see a reduction in the amount of repairs carried out at 1st and 2nd Line. The combat units will be moving so fast that a maintenance unit keeping up with them would have no time for repair work. While recovery assets will stay with units, it is likely that the future will see repair more centralised, on grounds of both cost and practicability. Consequently, units will have to be treated like ships; at certain times they will have to pull into a 'port' (a repair site) to be refitted.

The complexity and range of modern equipment also seems to be requiring the unit maintenance technician to be something of a 'Renaissance Man' which in turn requires almost degree level in mechanics, physics and elec-tronics. To produce such a soldier is expensive in time, as well as financially. The alternative, like the US Army, is to train mechanics just for one very narrow discipline or speciality. This is a particularly attractive option for conscript armies who have the manpower to afford numerically strong main-tenance units. Because the mechanic needs to know what is going on inside his Black Boxes, there is likely to be a growth in the 'operator-mechanic'. An operator-mechanic is one who both crews his equipment and is trained to repair it. Hitherto limited to very esoteric equipments, current practice has signals and air defence artillerymen trained both to operate their equipment and to maintain it. While there are costs involved in double training the unit soldier, these are offset by the savings in strictly maintenance manpower, who, in the strictest terms, do not add to the 'bayonet' strength of the unit they support. This trend is almost a reversion to the historical practice of each arm repairing its own equipment. The trend does not mean the end of the general maintenance function, but would reduce the apparent numbers of those involved in repair by showing operator-mechanics as part of the fight-ing strength of the units concerned.

7.

Medical Services

'The great thing in all military service is health'[1]

The requirement for armies to have an efficient medical service is self-evident. Nor is it just for the morale benefit. Historically, armies have suffered more casualties from poor hygiene and general medical complaints than they have from enemy action. Even today, every seven days an armoured division (about 14,000 men) is on exercise it can expect to have up to 500 soldiers report sick as a result of infection, routine disabilities and accidents. An efficient medical service is, therefore, vital to any army embarking on operations.

Cadreisation of Medical Units

All armies recognise the importance of an efficient medical service but the degree to which their aspirations can be met is governed, even more than for other military requirements, by what their nation can afford in the way of resources and expensively trained manpower. The latter is especially true of the armies of developing nations. Their nations rarely have enough medical cover for their civilian population, let alone their military. Consequently, the peacetime medical services of most armies are skeletal compared with their proper establishment for war. In almost every army the bulk of a nation's medical services come from the reserves. When operations short of general war and mobilisation take place it is inevitable that almost the first reservists to be called up will be medical personnel. The only British reservists it was found necessary to call up for the 1991 liberation of Kuwait were medical units, and this from a nation more used than most to mounting expeditionary forces. Even more endemic (to use a medical term) is the cadreisation of peacetime medical units. Thus, while it might appear that these units are regular and available for operations, they are more often than not at only 40 per cent of what should be their wartime strength. Unfortunately, medical units are amongst the most vulnerable category for peacetime cadreisation; for the restricted numbers of peacetime medics are normally sufficient to handle exercise and routine peacetime casualties. The greatest danger occurs when military planners believe that these numbers will also be enough for war. (See Figure 7.1.)

Location	Second World War	Present Day Peace Establishment	Present Day War Establishment
Company			
Stretcher bearers	4	Nil	Nil
Medics	Nil	Unit Corporal	Unit Corporal Medical Corporal
Regimental Aid Post			
Stretcher bearers	12	Nil	Nil
Medics	Doctor	Doctor	Doctor
	Medical Sergeant 2 x Orderly Driver	Unit Sergeant Unit Lance Corporal 3 x Unit Privates	Medical Sergeant Unit Sergeant Unit Lance Corporal 3 x Unit Privates

FIG. 7.1 Comparison of medical manpower for British Army major units Second World War and present day

Harsh Medical Facts

The late-twentieth-century soldier does not expect to be left to die of his wounds on the battlefield.[2]

There is a great similarity between the medical organisations of modern armies; more perhaps than in any other logistic sphere. This stems from some incontrovertible facts about the human body. The first of these is that a casualty operated upon within six hours of having been wounded has a much better chance of surviving. Consequently, most armies have a 'Six Hour Rule' and organise their 1st (unit level) and 2nd (brigade and divisional level) Line medical units so that the bulk of casualties can be given medical treatment within that period. The second is that, a casualty's chance of surviving the operation increases markedly if it is followed by a period of at least 10 days before movement is attempted; the 'Ten Day Rule'. Consequently, once forward medical units are loaded with casualties they cannot lightly be moved around the battlefield. The third fact is that a significant number of casualties can be lost during the recuperative process unless skilled and sustained nursing is provided. Lastly, especially in times of intensive casualties, the limited medical effort available cannot give full attention to each and every patient and some priority system has to be used to decide who receives that limited medical attention and when.

The First World War French army coined the term 'Triage' to describe the categorisation of casualties into one of three types: those for whom little or nothing can be done with what is available; those who can be saved if swift action can be taken; those who with the minimum of attention can safely be left to later treatment further back. Needless to say, history abounds with cases of patients classified as 'nothing can be done' who subsequently survived. But, harsh though it might appear, this classification of casualties as more likely to save life than to lose it. It concentrates limited medical attention on those who will benefit from it the most. Thus armies organise their medical services to provide only an evacuation system at 1st (Unit) and 2nd (Brigade and Division) Line, supplemented sometimes by small emergency surgical and post-operative facilities, and provide the first hospitals, Field and General, at 3rd (Corps) and 4th (Army or Base) Line.

1st Line Medical Units

At unit level the medical services, along with unit personnel, make up the regimental aid post; a small platoon or large section in size and based on two or three tracked or wheeled vehicles. This post takes in the casualties from the companies. It is important to remember that the bulk of fighting is done by the combat units and that, within these, it is the sub-units which are those most likely to be closely engaged with the enemy and thus to suffer the greater amount of casualties. This is not to say that other types of soldier will not be wounded; only that those the most likely to be wounded are those within the companies and squadrons of combat units.

Even in the most lavishly equipped armies, the company aid post, the only immediately available facility for the bulk of those likely to be wounded, will be just one vehicle manned by two or three men. When a soldier is wounded this vehicle could be away delivering an earlier casualty to the regimental aid post or pinned down by the tactical situation. Thus for the bulk of wounded soldiers the first person to try to treat their wounds will not be medically qualified. During the Lebanon War 80 per cent of all Israeli casualties received their initial treatment from non-medical personnel. This emphasises the need for first class first aid and casualty-handling training for individual combat soldiers at the company level. The British Army maxim is that such training can reduce subsequent mortality rates by as much as 40 per cent.

It is the regimental aid post that makes the first of the all important 'Triage' decisions. The regimental aid post takes as its guide that the most urgent type of patient to be examined are those with head or trunk wounds. These are the most likely areas where vital organs could have been damaged.

2nd Line Medical Units

Evacuation in tracked armoured ambulances to 2nd Line dressing stations is the next step. These come forward from 2nd Line to collect from the regimental aid post. As soon as operations allow, casualties are transferred to 2nd Line wheeled ambulances. These give a smoother and faster ride and are therefore much easier for the casualty. At the dressing stations the patient is

again categorised. Urgent cases are operated upon. There is, however, a limit
to the number that can be dealt with. Medical units in this role have very few
beds and may need to move, and thus cannot guarantee to provide the vital
post-operative stability that is needed under the Ten Hour Rule.

A dressing station's ability to handle casualties is governed by two factors:
the number of doctors within it and its holding of medical stores, especially
blood. Effective clinical judgements in the field are best made by rested men.
Treatment of casualties requires medical stores and blood and a dressing
station has only so much of these. Consequently, a rule of thumb for medical
units at this level might be that they should be expected to treat routinely
only 60 casualties per hour. After 600 casualties the unit has had enough;
doctors and medical stores are exhausted and no more patients should be
accepted.

3rd And 4th Line Medical Units

But the aim of all 1st and 2nd Line medical units is to so stabilise
casualties' conditions that evacuation to the 3rd and 4th Line larger and
static, field and general hospitals can take place. It is in these 400- and 800-
bed hospitals that the casualties can be best treated and cared for. They are
large and their ancillary facilities match the best of civilian hospitals, with
X-Ray, medical, physiotherapy and laboratory departments.

The field hospitals are grouped together in the corps area and make up a
forward surgical complex; it is these hospitals which primarily provide the
surgical facility in the combat area. They can have up to eight surgical teams
as their permanent establishment and be reinforced by more if need be.

The general hospitals are held further back in the corps area or behind it at
4th Line. They provide the long-term nursing and rehabilitation needed for
patients not otherwise able to survive the trip back to the Base. The aim of
both types of hospital is either to treat the casualty so that he can be returned
to duty or to stabilise his condition so that he can be evacuated out of the
combat area. Once at a Base or civilian hospital, his recuperation process can
start and his eventual return to duty can be ensured.

Casualty Evacuation by Air

If the key to the survival of most casualties is the time within which they
receive treatment (see Figure 7.2), then the speed of their evacuation from
the combat area to surgical and post-operative facilities is vital. Yet the
evacuation process outlined above is time-consuming; especially the moves in
tracked ambulances from the point of wounding, via the regimental aid post
to the exchange point where the casualties are cross-loaded into faster
wheeled ambulances.

Hitherto, armies were faced with either siting dressing stations out of
harm's way back in the divisional rear area, and thereby making it difficult
to meet the Six Hour Rule or, siting them further forward where they were

War	Mortality of wounded	Time spent in Transport (hours)
First World War	8.5%	12 - 18
Second World War	5.8%	1 - 12
Korean	2.4%	3 - 6
Vietnam	1.7%	1 - 4

FIG. 7.2 Transport timings and mortality of wounded[3]

1.   Evacuation is not urgent - primary treatment and preparation for evacuation is.
2.   Medical aid should be given in the most advanced position possible.
3.   Shock should be prevented by early and massive infusion of electrolytes.
4.   All severe casualties are to be accompanied by a medical team throughout the chain of evacuation.

FIG. 7.3 Israeli casualty treatment philosophy[3]

vulnerable to enemy action. Casualty evacuation by air has, to some extent, revolutionised this situation. Any of the evacuation methods outlined above can be short-circuited when weather and the operational air situation allow and when aircraft can be made available. But good weather and the availability of aircraft cannot always be guaranteed. Thus ground ambulances are still required. The Israeli Army appreciates this dilemma and has changed its procedure to giving skilled casualty treatment at the place of wounding. (See Figure 7.3.)

When they are flying and available, helicopters and aircraft are still limited in the number of casualties they can carry. This is less of a problem than it might seem. The prime candidates for aircraft evacuation are those in the Triage's 'need urgent treatment to be saved' category and these rarely form the bulk of casualties. As a guide, sitting or stretcher casualties can be evacuated by the helicopter types shown in Figure 7.4.

Casualty Estimates

There will be casualties in war: one's own, one's allies and those of the enemy. It is an army's job to try to make a worst case estimate of what they

Helicopter type	Sitting	Stretcher
Observation (eg. GAZELLE)	2 or 3	1
Older Light Utility (eg. SCOUT or ALOUETTE)	8	3
Modern Light Utility (eg. LYNX)	15	8 + 3 sitting
Medium Utility (eg. CHINOOK)	45	12 (but 24 could be carried with more attendants)

FIG. 7.4 Helicopter evacuation capabilities

Formation	Daily Average For All Days In Action	Severe Battle
Brigade	1.5%	12 - 15%
Division	1.0%	5 - 6%
Corps	0.5%	2 - 3%

FIG. 7.5 Second World War casualty estimates

might be. The medical services have to base their plans on what the tacticians predict will be the level of casualties. It is done this way because it is the tactical staff who have the best information on the relative balance of forces, the likely intensity of the conflict and the changes of success. Second World War casualty planning figures are shown in Figure 7.5.

These figures show that during this period, and possibly during likely future conflict, the majority of casualties occur at the 'sharp end' of the combat brigade level. Present day casualty computations are classified; for they are derived from an analysis of the effects of enemy weapons. However, because of the improved lethality and accuracy of modern weapon systems, present day planning figures must be higher than the Second World War rates.

Relatively recent conflicts have produced the casualty proportions for the British and US forces involved (with 40 per cent being stretcher cases and 50 per cent being sitting wounded) shown in Figure 7.6.

These casualty figures relate mostly to the winning side in each campaign; or at least to those who had the better medical evacuation and treatment

Conflict	Proportion
Second World War	1 to 3.1
Korea	1 to 4.1
Vietnam	1 to 5.6
Falkland Islands	1 to 3.8
Liberation of Kuwait	1 to 100

FIG. 7.6 Deaths to wounds casualty proportions in recent conflicts

chain. The casualty rates for defeat (wounded or dead) can be anything up to 30 per cent of the defeated force. Figures for the defeated Iraqi army in the liberation of Kuwait are not yet public but would seem to have been of this order.

The Falkland Islands and liberation of Kuwait figures, which derive from the special circumstances pertaining to each of these campaigns, deserve special analysis. In the Falkland Islands, all sources praise the efforts of the medical units involved[4] and state that everything that could be done was done. But the filthy climatic conditions and the desperate nature of the close quarter ground fighting must have increased the number of casualties.

In the 1991 liberation of Kuwait the limited opposition and duration of the conflict coupled with an extremely effective first aid training programme reduced Western Coalition forces' combat casualties to a remarkable degree. This was matched by an unprecedented drop in the number of routine casualties, ailments and accidents. The British forces involved lost fewer soldiers to road accidents than they would have expected to lose over a similar period back in their peacetime European barracks. Hot climates have devasted armies before but it seems that for the British Army an extremely effective hygiene campaign was waged. This, coupled with an extensive use of paper plates and plastic knives, reduced casualties from poor hygiene to below those expected on a European exercise; a remarkable success for the British medical services.

These two anomalous campaigns apart, the beneficial effects of improved medical techniques, the introduction of penicillin and anti-biotics and air evacuation of casualties are clear to see.

Combat Stress

The noise and impact of high intensity conflict can so affect soldiers that they become unable to handle the stress of battle. This phenomenon first came to prominence as 'shell shock' during the First World War. Earlier conflicts had probably had the same thing, but it was only its incidence during the intensive trench fighting of the First World War that forced medical men and, more importantly, commanders to acknowledge its existence. The incidence of 'combat stress', as it is now called, seems likely to be even greature in a future 24-hour high intensity conflict. A figure of 10 to 20 per cent of all battle casualties has been quoted.[5] This was certainly the aim of the Warsaw Pact, whose deliberate and declared policy was to bombard NATO troops so hard that 'battlefield paralysis' was achieved.

Modern medical thought now has it that there could well be three different types of combat stress. The first of these has been described as battle fatigue and is said to result from exhaustion and lack of sleep and to occur after about four days of heavy battle. It is relatively easy to cure. Rest is all that is needed. The next category is that of battle shock, sustained by soldiers exposed suddenly to the enormous strain of battle. Second World War histories all speak of the cataclysmic effects of concentrated artillery bombardments and how the defenders were numbed into submission by barrages. Battle shock does not seem to relate to the number of wounded. It is the shock of battle that causes a temporary psychological upset so that the soldier is unable to function normally. Lastly, there are true psychiatric casualties, where the patient suffers from a recognised psychiatric condition such as a depressive illness or an acute neurosis. Battle fatigue and battle shock are not psychiatric illnesses, although both could become so if remedial action is not taken.

As with many other medical conditions, with battle stress there can be prevention as well as cure. The condition arises in times of uncertainty, continued bombardment and fighting on a 24-hour battlefield which allows little, if any, time for relaxation and rest. There would seem to be three key elements to resisting battlefield stress: competence, good and confident leadership and unity amongst the group. Allied with these are efforts by commanders to ensure that, whatever the pressures, soldiers are allowed time for relaxation and, most importantly of all, deep restoring sleep. Yet even in the best led and organised of armies it is inevitable that modern warfare will create battle stress casualties. During the 1976 Yom Kippur War, when the Israeli Army had to meet the shock of an intensive and surprise assault, more than 900 of their first 1,500 casualties were caused by combat stress.[6]

Battle stress casualties will occur in future conflicts and a system and philosophy of treatment needs to be established. During the First World War the British Army treated stress casualties by evacuating them straight to United Kingdom civilian hospitals for treatment. By 1917, 20 per cent of the 200,000 soldiers on the British Army's pension list were said to be mental casualties,[7] some never recovered. The French Army tackled the problem differently. Stress casualties were only taken back to military hospitals near the front line where a level of military discipline was kept up. Seventy per cent of the French stress casualties improved.[8] It may seem harsh, but the moral of these two examples is clear. The nearer to the battle that treatment is given and the more military the atmosphere in which the casualty lives, the more there is a chance that the stress casualty will recover and return to duty.

As a result, modern armies now plan to treat combat stress casualties as far forward as possible. Treatment seems to be best based on the assumption that the soldier is going to recover. The process starts at the regimental aid post where, if possible, every stress casualty is held for up to 48 hours in this relatively 'quiet' area helping with menial tasks. Interestingly, staying within the same unit and the familiar work activity seems to overcome continued exposure to the horrors of war. Harder hit casualties would be held for up to two days at 2nd Line in what are now called 'Battleshock Rehabilitation Units'; these are manned by ordinary medical staff but supported by a field psychiatric team. There would need to be a number of these because the estimate of a maximum of 20 per cent of all casualties being cases of battle shock would mean that one installation would be swamped. Not all soldiers will recover in the divisional rear area and some will have to be evacuated to the general hospitals at 4th Line, which will need Battleshock Rehabilitation Units as well. The general hospitals will keep those casualties who seem likely to be able to return to duty within five to seven days but, if it is not possible to give psychiatric casualties the attention they merit, they will be evacuated out of theatre.

It is estimated that, if this treatment policy is followed, as many as 60 per cent of combat stress casualties might be returned to their units within four days and that another 10 per cent will be saved by the 3rd Line medical units. Above all, the lesson of history is clear. These casualties should not be treated differently. They should be treated as soldiers and everyone involved in their handling should stress the fact that they have a temporary disability which will pass shortly and that they will be able to return to their units soon. Treatment of combat stress casualties should not interfere with the treatment of physical casualties and, because speed of evacuation is not vital in their cases, they can await transport when it becomes available.

Nuclear, Biological and Chemical Casualties

If modern warfare has added combat stress to the challenges facing a modern army's medical function, it has also added the spectre of treating casualties in a nuclear, biological and chemical (or NBC) environment. In such cases the Triage decisions for a doctor are particularly hard and harsh to make. Medical staff could be faced with seemingly healthy soldiers who have been so irradiated that death is certain, whatever treatment is given to them. So far, modern armies have been mercifuly spared the horrors of biological warfare. Its effects can only be postulated. It would seem that, until vaccines are developed to counter the particular biological attack, medical facilities would be swamped by the likely casualty numbers.

The treatment of chemical casualties is much more practised. It was the stated policy of the Warsaw Pact to use chemical weapons so most NATO armies have studied the medical problems that might result. The successful treatment of chemical weapons casualties does require special medicines, equipment and procedures. There are preventative measures that can be taken to counter the effects of chemical warfare. Drugs such as atropine can counter some nerve agents, if taken in a timely fashion. Other drugs are available to build up individual resistance. There are special NBC casualty bags that enable a casualty to be protected and nursed at the same time.

A chemical attack, especially the first one in a conflict, could inflict mass casualties. Unfortunately, operating a medical facility in a chemical environment reduces the capacity of individual medical facilities by as much as 50 per cent. The need to maintain 'dirty' (contaminated) and 'clean' (uncontaminated) areas soaks up the medical manpower that should be treating casualties. Moreover, if casualties are 'dirty' they need to be decontaminated and this takes a lot of time and energy on the part of the medical personnel. Personnel who would be working at intensive and exhausting rates are not helped by their own need to wear protective equipment and to take protective measures. Most military men, more than any civilian, pray that nuclear, biological and chemical weapons will never be used. They appreciate the effects of them all too well.

PLATE 16   A German Army *Elefant* 50 tonne tank transporter. In this case carrying a German Army *Kampfpanzer Leopard A1*. The weight of modern main battle tanks when full with ammunition precludes all but a very few specialised civilian vehicles carrying them. Consequently, armies have had to invest in very expensive specialised tank transporters. (*K. Zeisig*)

PLATE 17   A modern all-wheel-drive fuel tanker. As the number of vehicles in armies has grown then so has the requirement for fuel to power them. Civilian industry does not have the all-terrain mobility requirement of armies and all-wheel-drive fuel tankers are almost exclusively military specials. (*H. Bentley-Marchant*)

PLATE 18 A British Army Ramp Powered Lighter. Interestingly, armies seem to love acquiring water-borne vessels. The British Army has a fleet which includes ocean going vessels! (*H. Bentley-Marchant*)

PLATE 19 A German Army *Bergepanzer Standard* tracked recovery and repair vehicle. Shown here lifting the power pack of a *Kampfpanzer Leopard A1* whilst carrying a replacement power pack on its rear deck. The author has seen German Army maintenance troops carry out such a change, and the repaired tank drive away, all in five minutes. There was, however, just the slight suspicion that everything had been prepared for such a demonstration and that, in the field, routine power pack changes might take a little longer! (*K. Zeisig*)

PLATE 20 A British Army Beach Armoured Recovery Vehicle (BARV). Specialised climates and terrain can require specialist recovery vehicles. The BARV was introduced to recover tanks broken down in the surf of a beach landing under fire. Because of its weight it cannot float. Instead it wades through the surf. Hence its high superstructure. (*A.C.D. Welch*)

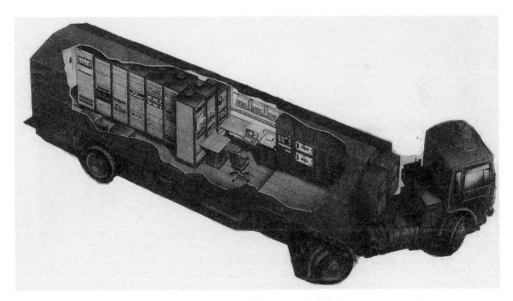

PLATE 21 A German Army *Remus* Electronics Repair Trailer. Computer controlled measuring and testing systems diagnose the faults in electronic sub-assemblies which are then exchanged for serviceable ones. A similar British Army vehicle costs over $4M. (*M.H.G. Ziegler*)

PLATE 22
The British Army
COFFER field
computer system.
This is the British
Army's combat
logistic area units'
spare parts computer.
The computer is
housed in the vehicle
on the right. On the
left is the *British
Army Transferable
Stores Container*;
a revolutionary way of
storing spare parts
which reduces wasted
space inside the
container by having
movable shelving.
(*Author*)

PLATE 23 A military postal depot. Military postal services are under the same pressure to reduce manpower levels as the rest of armies. The good news is that this means that expensive labour saving technology is bought to equip the military main peacetime postal sorting depot. The bad news is that it is rarely possible for this equipment to be picked up and deployed in a Theatre of Operations. (*M. Gilbertson*)

PLATE 24 Labour personnel rigging a helicopter underslung load. In this case a British Army 1 tonne Landrover to be carried by a German *CH 53* Medium Transport Helicopter, true interoperability. Preparing helicopter loads is labour intensive and requires skill. (*Author*)

PLATE 25 US Army Meal Ready To Eat. The famous *MRE* – nicknamed 'Meals Rejected by Ethiopians' by the US soldiers forced to eat them for the long months prior to the Liberation of Kuwait 1991. Interestingly, during the same campaign, the British Army seemed to be much more content with its *COMPO* rations. The way the *COMPO* was prepared, varied and served by the British Army Catering Corps probably had a lot to do with this. (*R. Smith*)

PLATE 26 A field kitchen. The morale and hygiene effect of well cooked food in the field can be drastically underestimated. (*N. Shephard*)

PLATE 27 A field petroleum site. Fuel is the lifeblood of a mechanised army. This site is that of one of the petroleum companies of the British 6 Ordnance Battalion (a 3rd Line supply unit) during the Liberation of Kuwait 1991. (*A. Taylor*)

PLATE 28   A British Army Rail Transfer Equipment. Modern war demands vast tonnages of ammunition. Rail is used to carry these tonnages to as close to the front line as possible. But at some stage the ammunition has to be off-loaded and put onto vehicles or stored in dumps. Specialised rough terrain rail transfer equipment has been introduced to speed up this lengthy and vulnerable process. (*Author*)

PLATE 29   The German Army *MULTI* system. The need to move vast tonnages has forced most armies to adopt a demountable rack off-loading and pick-up system. (*H.G. Ziegler*)

PLATE 30   Royal Air Force *Chinook* with underslung load. The helicopter can assist logisticians in all the phases of war and is especially useful for quick reaction tasks. However, it carries relatively little (8 tonnes underslung for a *Chinook*) and needs a substantial and expensive logistic tail to keep it flying. (*Author*)

8.

The Smaller Logistic Functions

There are a host of small administrative functions needed by an army at war that do not neatly fall into the four main logistic functions of supply, transport and movements, repair and recovery and medical services. These may be relatively small functions but their importance to the wellbeing of an army at war should not be underestimated.

Post

Mail, and the contact with home that it brings, is vital to the soldier in the field. Armies at war know that the regular and routine arrival of mail is a major means of sustaining morale. Modern armies, even with their sophisticated and more worldly-wise soldiers, regard the prompt and routine dispatch and arrival of mail as one of the most important things in the combat soldier's daily calender. The distribution challenge this poses for the military postal services is a stiff one.

The movement of mail from the home base to the theatre of operations is, however, a relatively simple task. Most armies have a peacetime postal depot manned by soldiers located in a suitable communications nodal point. More often than not this depot is in the national capital city, which is normally the centre-point for the civilian postal service. This is the case for the British Army but the US Army has main postal depots, for understandable geographical and historical reasons, on both its east and west coasts. The collocation of the civilian and military postal centres at the nub of a nation's communications system makes obvious sense and can mean a reduction of at least 24 hours in the time a letter takes to get to a soldier. Such sites are, however, costly in real estate terms and potentially lucrative if sold. In peacetime, armies regularly fight off government financiers seeking to make savings by moving their postal centre out of its central location to somewhere cheaper but more remote, which would add to the time it takes mail to get to the soldiers.

Military postal services all maintain in peace a system of addresses based on unit titles:

A Company
1st Infantry Battalion
Forces Post Office 22

as well as one based on the actual barrack address of the unit involved. The unit title address is the system that would be used for war, when security would restrict giving the obvious detail of a unit's location. These cryptic addresses are, however, used surprisingly often in time of peace. For, despite what might be thought, a complete military unit is not often in its peacetime location. Exercises, deployments abroad and sudden emergency tours mean that a battalion might be in its barracks for only six months in a year. Consequently, the peacetime military postal services are well practised in the system they would have to adopt for war. On mobilisation, of course, all the field postal numbers are changed for security reasons.

On operations, the sorting of mail at the main military postal depots is relatively simple. Instead of a myriad of individual addresses, military sorters have just to use the field post office numbers allocated to each area of operations. Sorted into batches, the mail is then taken to airports (for almost all military mail in war goes by air) and flown in either military or contractors' aircraft to the theatre of operations.

It is in the theatre of operations that the military postal services' problems start. The first problem is to find out the current location of the unit involved, for military men delight in moving units from the command of one formation to another, or moving the complete formation to some other area. So the postal services have to work out how long the mail is likely to take to get to the front and must then find out where the unit concerned will be at that time. This, as can be imagined, is sometimes a detective task worthy of an Inspector Maigret: its solution is one of the marks of a successful postal services commander.

The postal services make their best guess and then start on their second problem; which is finding the transport to carry the mail forward. Armies are bedevilled by the fact that transport moving back is normally empty, for it has delivered its loads, but transport moving forward is invariably full of supplies or reinforcements, and has little spare capacity. Moving mail from the air-head or point of entry to the corps area is not normally a problem. If trains cannot be used then local resources, either hired vehicles or the civilian mail service itself, or military transport can be tasked. But the further forward one goes in the logistic chain the less easy it is to find transport and manpower that does not have an urgent operational task. Even so, wise commanders insist that transport is provided; as little as four cargo vehicles a day could be sufficient to carry the mail for one division or, alternatively, support helicopters could be tasked.

Whichever means of transport is used, the mail is sent to the logistic control point for the formation concerned. At the corps control point there would be the equivalent of a small postal company. This would sort the mail for the units in the corps area, and notify them of its arrival, and forward the mail for formations to the logistic control point of the formation concerned. At the divisional logistic control point would be a small eight-man postal detachment whose prime task is to keep track of the locations of the logistic control points of the brigades and to monitor just what units are in those brigades. The detachment sorts the mail for the units in the divisional rear area and puts the brigade mail into bags for that brigade. Transport then has to be found to take it to their logistic control points.

At the brigade logistic control points, another eight-man postal detachment will receive the mail, sort it into unit bags, if this has not been done already, and then pass it to the units' brigade rear elements for passage forward. In the rear elements the mail is again sorted into sub-unit bundles and passed forward along with the nightly resupply to the companies. The companies then distribute the mail to the platoons along with the resupply and, at last, the soldier gets his letter. From arrival in theatre to arrival with the soldier, the mail can take three days or more. Support helicopters can short-circuit this time. But their use involves risk. If the unit is not at the helicopter's destination or has moved, mail for the unit can bounce around the combat area trying to find a home, and can take even longer to arrive with the soldier than if it had awaited a more mundane sort of carrier.

Mail from the soldier to home is easier to handle. The system works in reverse and becomes more manageable the further back one goes. Transport for the return trip, with lots of empty vehicles having discharged their loads, is easier to find. Less appreciated is the sheer volume that the military postal service has to carry. In addition to the obvious private mail is the operational correspondence of an army at war (one attack could involve the movement of 60 copies of the operations order concerned) and its logistic correspondence; low priority spares demands, for example, will all be sent in the mail.

Even less appreciated is that all these little postal detatchments replicate the functions of a civilian post office. The variety of the tasks performed, the amounts of money that can accrue and the detective work and motivation involved in ensuring that the mail gets to the right place means that the non-commissioned officers in charge of these little detachments have to be very special men indeed.

Catering

The importance of a nutritional and balanced diet to a combat soldier is self-evident. Most armies have complete ready-to-eat meals which are based on estimates of the calorific intake needed for soldiers in action. The British Army has five types, shown in Figure 8.1.

In such packs, the menus are designed for national tastes. Except for those foods which need rehydration (particularly Arctic or cold weather packs which clearly cannot have any liquids otherwise they would freeze), the meals in the packs can be eaten hot or cold and if eaten regularly should give troops enough calories to keep them at operational efficiency for up to 30 days. But after 30 days on this sort of ration intestinal complaints can start

Type	Number of types of Menu	Nutritional Data per man/day and Energy			
		Protein	Fat	CHO	K cal
10 man (General Purpose)	7	12%	36%	52%	3480
4 man (Armoured Vehicle Crews)	7	12%	36%	52%	3480
24 Hour General Service	4	12%	26%	62%	4750
24 Hour Arctic	4	12%	26%	62%	4750
24 Hour General Purpose	7	12%	33%	55%	4600

FIG. 8.1 British Army operational ration packs

and soldiers become bored with the limited menus available. As a result, armies try to put off using these packs for as long as possible. This causes problems because the handling of fresh rations requires specific skills and equipment; butchery for instance, and refrigerated containers. Fresh rations occupy at least three times the space of operational ration packs; which means more transport is needed. Even when only ration packs are being used, a wise commander supplements their contents with as many fresh items as he can.

With the existence of operational ration packs the uninitiated might query why a catering service is needed at all. Yet, like most things done by armies that appear to be just tradition-based, there are sound and practical reasons for the tying up of valuable resources in a logistic service that would appear to have little combat benefit. Despite the introduction of ready-to-eat army rations, the preparation of food takes time, and the cooking of it on a myriad of small fires is both wasteful and dangerous. Sometimes it is time that can be ill-afforded. Then there is the soldier's traditional approach to field hygiene. Anyone who has eaten that most delightful battlefield snack, a fried egg sandwich produced by a tank crew, will remember those delightfully black crunchy bits; the uncleaned detritus of a hundred similar meals. Hygiene-related illnesses have been the most significant part of casualty lists since warfare began. Present-day stomachs are perhaps more susceptible than their forebears; perhaps because they are used to purer water supplies. The US Army reported that 40 to 50 per cent of some of their units in the liberation of Kuwait were affected by diarrhoea. Most of the sick had at least one day off duty, some up to a week, and others had to be evacuated out of Saudi Arabia.[1]

Lastly, attractively presented, good food and the 'bonding' effect of eating together, is good for morale. This should not be underestimated. Modern warfare is a fragmented affair. Tactics and working practices force dispersion. This dispersion increases isolation and is a contributory factor to stress. The communal meal reduces this isolation and reinforces group identity; indeed, some units only ever see most of their comrades at mealtimes. So for a combination of pragmatic and morale reasons every unit in the army will have its small catering platoon and will revert from detachment cooking (where crews feed themselves) to central cooking under the catering platoon at every opportunity.

Labour Services

The mechanisation of the modern world and its reliance on the internal combustion engine, plus the cost of labour in Western economies, has led Western military men to forget just what can be done by enough pairs of hands.[2] Despite a widespread use of mechanical and container handling devices, like the rough terrain fork-lift truck, almost every enterprise could use more labour, especially modern Western armies where establishments have been reduced to the bone. The repetition of 'Western' in this listing is deliberate. Third World armies, by force of circumstance and perhaps inclination, have not forgotten the power of bare hands. Often this has come as a shock to the Western army facing them which, discovering massive underground tunnel systems or extensive field entrenchments, marvel at the fact that it was done without the mechanical aids on which they are so reliant. For all armies, labour services can help by either providing labour itself or by controlling civilian contractors.

There has been argument that a labour corps, *per se*, is not needed in war. It is held that there will be more than enough reservists, especially of the older sort, who could be used as labour. Conversely, to use trained reservists in this way might be wasteful. They would have military and technical skills that might make them more useful in another role. But history shows that armies at war need vast amounts of labour and that this labour need have very little, if any, military training.

An even greater case could be made that there is no need for armies to have a labour corps in peace. Peacetime labour tasks can easily be done by contracted civilian labour and, because of the cost comparison between a soldier and a civilian, more cheaply. Even if enough money existed to pay for soldiers, most armies would rather have a battalion of infantry, or drivers, that could be put to labouring tasks rather than have a Labour Service battalion that was only capable of labouring.

It is sometimes forgotten that modern peacetime armies employ a vast number of civilians in the support area and the drive to reduce 'Tail-to-Teeth' ratios has accentuated this. The 1990 British Army supply service had some 6,000 soldiers. It employed 13,000 civilians; more than twice its number of soldiers. The control and the legislative restrictions about civilian employment means that an army needs specialists in this area. Usefully, too, such skills can be carried over into wartime when there will be a clear requirement to have military labour in wartime to fill the gaps in the support area, especially 3rd and 4th Line, where successive reductions have left all the logistic services desperately slim.

The sum of these factors is that there is a requirement for labour services in peace and war. In peace time, however, for such a service to be completely military is nonsense; it would be unnecessarily expensive. One solution would be to have military specialists in this field employed in peace time controlling the large numbers of civilians now employed by armies. In war these specialists could control the military and civilian labour that would so obviously be needed.

9.

Logistic Support for the Phases of War

The Time Factor

Of all the warlike actions known to man, logistics seems the most likely to be the one which could be described as a 'science', when the normal description of conflict is of 'the art of war'. The constituent parts of logistics lend themselves to computation and to statistics. A vehicle takes a certain minimum time to load and unload. It can only carry a fixed amount. Military road movement can only be carried out at certain speeds and all logistic timings are affected by darkness. Taking these basic equations, it might not seem difficult to produce tables for what can be done, with an allowance for enemy action and accidents, which should allow anyone to become a logistician.

Unfortunately, the logistic support of operations is not as simple as this. At the unit level the logistician's task is very much a responsive one concerned with the current action and its aftermath. Combat sub-units are replenished as they near empty, and the empty resupply vehicles are themselves filled. There are the problems of enemy action, which routes are open and out of enemy artillery fire but, overall, the problems are relatively simple and require the unit level logistician to look only a little ahead. The further back one goes, though, the less clear the logistician's task becomes.

Level of Command	Tactician Looks Ahead	Logistician Looks Ahead
Brigade	6 - 30 hours	36 - 48 hours
Division	12 - 48 hours	60 - 72 hours
Corps	24 - 96 hours	84 hours - 5 days
Army	48 hours - 8 days	2 weeks - 3 months

FIG. 9.1 The logistic time factor in war

At the brigade level the logistic staff are planning beyond the current operation to the next; worrying about where the logistic units should be moved to in order to support the next action. At the divisional level, the logistic staffs are looking even further forward, to possible operations which are days ahead. Corps and army staffs are controlling current resupply, planning for firm operations and contingency planning for operations their formations might undertake in the days ahead. The mills of logistics grind small, and very slowly. Once logistic orders are issued it will take time before the logistic convoys can be loaded, given their orders and sent on their way. It will take them longer to move along the routes, off-load and return and it will take time to prepare the loads for use by the combat units. Even at unit level, where response should be the swiftest, logistics takes time. Two examples serve to underline this. The first is a broken-down tank within a tank company. It will take time for the tasking to be passed over the radio net to the repair and recovery team; logistic radio traffic is invariably accorded a lower priority than operations traffic. The details of the breakdown have to be passed to the repair team, who then have to decamouflage their vehicle and set off on their way. Even if there are no mishaps in the link-up between the repair team and the vehicle casualty, this process would take not less than half an hour, and often much longer; and this is before the team have even started repairing the tank. Depending on what is needed, the repair, if it can be made at all at this level, can take up to six hours but will almost never take less than 30 minutes to fix. So, even if everything were to go well and the repair team found the broken-down vehicle on its doorstep and the team had the right spares to repair the defect, it will be not less than an hour and a half before the tank can start rolling again. The second example relates to a request for anti-tank missiles for a hard-pressed infantry company. The immediate source would probably be a reserve of these missiles back at battalion level. The message has to be passed back, the resupply crew briefed and the missiles loaded, all of which takes time. Then there is the journey to the company which, if all goes well, will not take less than half an hour. Once in the company area a link-up has to be made with the company's resupply team and the missiles transloaded. Once again, a logistic task which, even if everything were to go well, would take not less than an hour and a half.

All this logistic activity will be complicated by the fact that logistic convoys and units are vulnerable. Logistic units can only really count on darkness for anything like safe movement. It would be the same for the rear areas, unless overwhelming air superiority is held. Furthermore, the routes themselves will not be empty. Coming back from the front line will be personnel and vehicle casualties and empty resupply vehicles. Reserve units and formations will be jostling for road space and redeploying combat formations will be blocking vital road junctions. The enemy, too, will have a hand to play and one carefully placed 'smart' weapon on a bridge or culvert could block a route to low mobility resupply vehicles.

On the credit side, a lot of very skilled and experienced logistic commanders and staff will be resolving the sort of conflicts that might result, and units and formations will have their on-hand stocks to help them survive any interruption in the logistic chain. But the fact remains that logistics is not an immediately responsive business and it takes time. Consequently, logisticians at the various levels try to look ahead, and almost invariably the period looked at has to be further forward than that of the tactician. (See Figure 9.1)

Routine Combat Holdings

The basic framework for a modern military formation in action is remarkably similar, whichever army is examined. All share, although they may call them by different names, the four lines of logistic support and have similar logistic command and control points. All strive to give each line of logistic support some degree of self-sufficiency to allow for the unexpected and for interruptions to the logistic supply chain.

Line of Logistic Support	Combat Supplies Holdings
1st Line (Unit level)	Up to 5 days
2nd Line (Brigade and Divisional level)	Up to 3 days
3rd Line (Corps level)	Up to 3 days
4th Line (Army level)	Holds Theatre reserve of at least 14 days but overall stocks held will depend on the time taken for supplies to transit from the base to the Theatre. This movement increment is additional to the Theatre reserve stocks.
Base	30 days stock for Army world - wide minus that held at 1st - 4th Line.

FIG. 9.2 Holdings of combat supplies

The actual holdings at each level depend upon what the nation concerned decided to spend on logistic self-sufficiency in peace time and the amount of transport lift available upon mobilisation. As a rule of thumb, formations would wish to hold the amount of war-like supplies necessary to enable them to fight for a number of 'battle' days. An example of how much might be held at each level is given in Figure 9.2.

Just what comprises a 'routine' battle day is difficult to estimate. One combat unit might be in reserve and fire nothing. Another might be in a quiet part of the front and fire relatively little. Yet another unit might find itself at the enemy's point of main effort and have to fire off just about everything that it has just to survive. These battle days are, therefore, nothing more than guide-lines to decide unit establishments in peace time and to provide a basis for logistic planning in war. During operations the logistician has to maintain the ability to switch supplies around the battlefield to ensure they end up where they are needed most.

The speed of modern tactical movement and the need to switch supplies to where they are most needed requires that 1st and 2nd Line supplies should be kept on the backs of the cargo vehicles carrying them – 'held on wheels'. To do so, however, would give combat units a massive logistic tail, which would be difficult to manoeuvre and all too easy for the enemy to target. Armoured infantry units will probably be able to carry their three-days' worth, their only problems being the bulky anti-tank missiles and the heavy mortar ammunition. Tank units will find it more difficult to carry all their three-days' worth and are more likely to be able to carry only what they think might be needed for two days. The size and weight of their main armament rounds is the biggest problem they face. As a guide, the contents of eight 8-tonne cargo vehicles and one 22,500 litre fuel tanker a day would normally be enough to sustain during daylight hours a single battalion-sized armoured infantry or tank unit in most types of action. Artillery units plan to fire at such intensive rates that even a large logistic wheel tail could carry only between half-a-day and a day's worth of what is thought needed. Consequently, even at the divisional 2nd Line level, it is inevitable that there will be large grounded stock areas sometimes holding more than two days' worth of the division's artillery ammunition and elements of the division's other requirements.

Unless the Soviet solution of fighting formations until their supplies are exhausted and then passing a fresh and fully supplied formation through to carry on the advance is adopted, armies have little alternative other than to ground-dump stocks and to attempt to continously resupply the formations in contact. This requires relatively safe areas for ground-dumped stocks and routes for the movement of those stocks, known as MSRs (Main Supply Routes).

Main Supply Routes

Main Supply Routes and their feeder railway routes are the main arteries of an army at war. Each formation would like to have at least two, with lateral 'feeder' routes. But they need to be capable of sustaining heavy and continuous traffic and to be able to take the weight of the heaviest vehicles within the formation; normally the weight of a tank-transporter carrying a 'bombed-up' main battle tank. Thus the bridges on these routes have to be capable of taking up to 70 tonnes. Even in Western Europe such routes are difficult to find and, elsewhere, the first requirement of an army's engineers is to build them or to upgrade existing routes to be able to take the required weight and volume of traffic. This can become a logistic factor which affects the result of wars. Like human arteries, these routes can clog around traffic

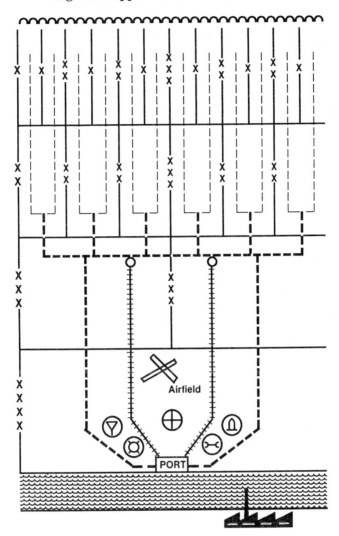

Fig. 9.3 Main supply routes

nodal points like bridges or as the result of accidents or enemy action, and one of the principal skills of a modern armoured commander is the ability to keep these open and flowing. One of General Schwartzkopf's unsung heroes during the liberation of Kuwait was the military policeman responsible for keeping open the main coast road from Al Jubayl northwards to Kuwait, not only for US Army traffic but also for the US Marines and some of the Coalition allies. For the British force, it was their only MSR.

Rommel, Patton and Zhukov all had the skill to keep armoured forces moving. One of Montgomery's most professional actions, perhaps more correctly credited to the movements staff at Lord Gort's Headquarters British Expeditionary Force (who were the ones that actually did the planning) took place in the retreat to Dunkirk in 1940. His 3rd Division was on the right of the British line. The collapse of the Belgian Army required him, in one night, to move his division across the line of communication of two corps in contact with the enemy and take up a position on the extreme left of the British line in order to fill the vacuum left by the Belgian Army. If a whole brigade travels along one road it would take about three hours to pass a single point. Montgomery's division had three brigades and enough divisional troops to amount to the equivalent of another brigade. On one route the division could have taken as much as 12 hours to pass over a road junction. Because it was moving laterally to the front, this meant that each of the fighting corps could have had half a day with no casualty evacuation and no resupply. The front could have buckled. It did not. One reason was that Montgomery had ensured his divisional headquarters was staffed with the pick of the available peace-time British regular army. They moved the division on a number of routes and crossed the other two corps' routes where they would cause the least delay. Another reason was Montgomery himself. Military historians will always argue whether he rates a place amongst the great military commanders of all time. None of them would, however, argue that he was not a master of the soldier's trade and he certainly proved it with this move. The move was successful and the logistic resupply of the two fighting corps was uninterrupted.

Logistic Control Points

If these MSRs are the arteries of an army at war, they are also its skeleton. The framework of the logistic support is built up, for obvious reasons, around them. Where these MSRs enter a formation's area is clearly a critical logistic control point. It is at these 'tradesman's entrances' to formations that resupply can be redirected to where it is needed most. Each formation at every level has at least one; with probably another for the bulky engineer items.

It is hard to impress on those that have not seen them just how important these control points are. Once inside a formation's area, vehicles and even whole convoys can fail to link up with fast-moving formations and units or they can just simply get lost. The logistic control points are the first stop for somebody trying to track them down. It can take a long time for a convoy to move up from 3rd Line to 2nd Line. In that time the situation can change and the convoys would need to be redirected. It is the logistic control points that help to do this. Lastly, there will be individual reinforcements and items such as engines and main assemblies that just get dumped at the control point to await unit collection. So a divisional logistic control point could have detachments from the military police, the transport corps, the supply corps and the postal service. The stores park of a divisional control point would cover not less than the equivalent of two football pitches and to camouflage this is a big task.

The large resupply convoys are rarely sent direct to units. More normally they enter the formation area through the logistic control point and move to

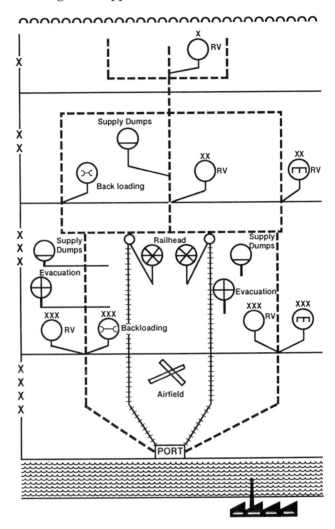

FIG. 9.4 Logistic control points

ground stock holding areas, dump their loads and then scurry back down the MSR to pick up their next load. In the divisional ground-dumped areas the suppliers will take the loads, previously configured for ease of transportation and safety, and form them into fireable loads for use by the combat units. Once this is done, and this takes some time, the smaller nightly resupply convoys will come and collect the stocks and take them to the brigade logistic control points where they get their final instructions as to their eventual destination.

The MSR network, the grounded stock locations and the loaded logistic vehicles, the logistic headquarters and the logistic control points together make up the basic fabric of the logistics of a military formation at war. This fabric, though, has to be tailored to the specific type of operation the army is conducting. These types of operation are called phases of war.

The NATO Phases of War

Military men argue their dogma just as much as anyone else. One of the many NATO successes has been to get some agreed terminology between the NATO nations. This did not come easy. Committee after committee studied the various subjects and, in the end, it was almost exhaustion that secured agreement. NATO started first with tactical terminology and it is in this area that the most advances have been made. It is now agreed amongst the NATO nations that there are three phases of war (the British Army used to have seven). These are listed in Figure 9.5.

Offensive Operations

Defensive Operations

Delaying Operations

FIG. 9.5 The NATO phases of war

NATO has also agreed that there are a number of 'Transitional Operations' which link the Phases of War. These are listed at Figure 9.6.

Advance to Contact

Meeting Engagements

Link-up Operations

Isolated Operations

Relief in Place

Forward Passage of Lines

Rearward Passage of Lines

FIG. 9.6 NATO transitional operations

All the phases of war and types of transitional operation produce logistic problems and it is the fabric of the basic logistic organisation, largely unamended, that is used to solve them.

Offensive Operations

Armies divide offensive operations into what they call the 'Quick' or 'Hasty' attack and the 'Deliberate' attack. The quick or hasty attack is one that is mounted with little preparation, especially logistically. Most readers will be aware of the military maxim that a superiority of three to one is needed before there is a reasonable degree of certainty of success for an attacker. Examination of successes by weaker attackers normally shows that, despite their numerical disadvantage, they were able to mass a decisive three to one advantage, or more, at the critical point in the battle. The defence, whilst it often loses the initiative, gains the advantage of being able to dig itself in. This protection for its forces increases the combat factor of each defensive element. Consequently, armies are loth to allow their opponents to settle in a defended position; for every day allowed to a defence to improve its defences means it becomes a harder nut to crack. Hence the hasty or quick attack.

Ostensibly the quick attack should present little problem to the logistician. This is true of the attack itself. Because of its lack of preparation, the units and formations involved will carry out the assault using only the supplies and assets they have with them. There is little time for routine resupply to fill any empty gaps. But equally, because of the lack of preparation, things are likely to go wrong, tactically and logistically. Supply, transport and medical commanders have to be especially alert and hold uncommitted assets as far forward as possible; otherwise they will not arrive in time to help the attack or the casualties resulting from it. The real logistic challenge comes after the attack has gone in. Low on ammunition and weakened by personnel and fighting vehicle casualties, the attacking formation is now very vulnerable until it has been replenished. Unfortunately, the resupply convoys to do this are probably struggling through routes blocked or damaged in the battle. Routes, if the attack is to be continued, become further crowded by the next formation to pass through, or the convoys of defence stores and mines waiting to set up and secure the newly-gained position. In such circumstances, the logistic priority must be the evacuation back of the attacking formation's personnel casualties, followed by the passage of the reserve formation or the movement of the defence stores.

Although most readers will have experienced similar problems on their local freeway, autobahn, autoroute or autostrada, there is often some difficulty in understanding the difficulties of military route control and congestion. The number, type and speed of the vehicles in an armoured infantry or tank battalion on one route could take up to 30 minutes to pass a particular point on the route. There are normally three or four such units in a brigade. This means that, if there is only one route, the brigade and its attached logistic assets (the equivalent of at least another major unit) could take up to three hours to pass a single point; this without any counter-action by the enemy. Clearly, the more routes that are open the swifter will be the passage of the brigade; but it is unlikely that at first there will be many routes open through the enemy position. Consequently, logistic resupply of the assaulting formation could have to wait three hours before the routes are clear enough for it to move forward to replenish.

If the logisticians' challenge comes in the aftermath of the hasty assault, it also comes in the preparatory stages of the deliberate attack. Such an attack presupposes an unsuccessful hasty assault and an enemy who has had time to dig-in and prepare his positions. Consequently, the weight of artillery fire necessary to neutralise the defence will be considerable and casualties amongst the assaulting force can be expected to be heavy. Consequently, the logistician's task is to bring forward artillery ammunition to dumps closer to the front and to ensure that enough medical units are deployed to treat the expected casualties. One of the major difficulties will be to gain enough road space in the limited area in front of the objective for the ambulance and resupply convoys to get through. Another will be that, having ground-dumped ammunition alongside guns, enemy locating units will find the artillery and counter-battery fire will force them to decamp. At worst the dumped ammunition will be lost to enemy fire. At best the ammunition has to be abandoned and a logistician will have to remember to pick it up after the battle has moved on. This is a particular problem in the withdrawal where the defender cannot come back to an artillery fire position. Unless care is taken, a significant amount of ammunition can be lost in this way.

All this logistic preparation could alert the enemy to the coming attack. Care has to be taken to preserve security and to carry out logistic activity within the screen of daily replenishment and to ensure that any logistic dumps are well camouflaged. Perhaps the best way to cloak the imminence of an attack is to make no overt logistic preparations at all at the divisional level. Instead, logistic assets could start to roll forward immediately action is joined. 2nd Line transport could go straight to the guns (who will probably have just enough to sustain them until the 2nd Line resupply arrives) and 3rd Line transport could come forward into the divisional area to establish completely new dumps just behind the assaulting troops. At least in this fashion, enemy intelligence at worst would only pick up the activity at the corps level, but would not be certain which one of that corps' divisions would be involved.

Defensive Operations

There are similar distinctions between the hasty and the deliberate defence. Both presuppose that the defender is losing, or at least is inferior to the enemy. Logistic assets will have been reduced and there will be few spare resources. Conversely, there are logistic advantages to the defence. Lines of supply will have been shortened and will be well known to the logistic troops. Shortened lines of supply mean quicker turn around times for logistic transport and this means they may be able to deliver more than usual.

Of the two types of defence it is the hasty defence which causes the biggest logistic problem, quite adequately described by the title, 'hasty'. The logistic priority goes first to the delivery of the defence stores and mines that can so transform the combat power of a dug-in force. Simultaneously, there is a desperate need to dump artillery ammunition near to where the guns will be or are firing, to clear the workshops of repairable vehicles (each one of which will be worth its weight in gold to the defender) and to empty the dressing stations of patients so that they are ready to receive the inevitable casualties from the battle to come. All other logistic functions take a back seat to these but, as battle is joined, the priorities become the evacuation of the new battle's casualties with continued resupply to the artillery in addition to resupply to the infantry (anti-tank missiles) and of main armament rounds for the tank units.

The deliberate defence produces problems similar to the hasty defence, but all doubled in scope and scale. The same priorities apply for the stages of the action but, in general, once action is joined the normal fabric of the logistic system can handle the logistic requirements of the battle. Two factors about this sort of action, however, require highlighting. They both stem from the fact that the enemy's surveillance assets will have spent some time searching out routine resupply routes and logistic unit locations. Unit logistic assets should be sited out of enemy field gun range, no nearer than 15 km to the front (unless masked by a terrain feature) and the 2nd Line dumps and logistic units should be sited about 25 km from the front line out of range of the enemy's heavy-depth fire artillery. As weapon ranges increase, so do these safety distances. Similarly, alternate resupply routes need to be chosen and brought into use once battle is joined. Otherwise the enemy will pinpoint the routine routes and the logistic resupply convoys will find themselves destroyed as soon as they move into enemy artillery range.

Delaying Operations

Any war of movement is testing for a logistician. At least in the advance the logistician's side is winning and the challenges will be those of success. In delaying operations, the logistician has all the challenges of a war of movement. There is also the likelihood that success is eluding his side, which is probably outnumbered. Thus there will be a considerable air threat and the constant menace of stocks being overrun. It has been said that delaying operations are perhaps the greatest challenge for tactical commanders. So they are for the logistician supporting him. The resources allocated to the preparation of the main defensive position must be balanced against those allocated to the force which is to buy time for the construction of that position. An average of about one third of the available force is traditionally allocated to the delaying task; customarily it is a tank heavy formation, as infantry formations are better employed digging-in on the main defensive position. As a result, the logistician's attention is split three ways; the moving back of the logistic stocks that are held forward, the support of the delaying force and the support to the formations allocated to the main defensive position. Logistic planning is further constrained by the fact that a logistic unit which is moving is unlikely to be doing any productive work.

Using an armoured division as an example, with an armoured brigade of its three brigades being the delaying force, the ideal move back would be phased, possibly over two nights. To do this too overtly could, however, let the enemy know that a withdrawal is planned. Consequently, the first night's rearward movement would be limited to logistic unit reconnaissance and advance parties. Very useful logistic work could, however, be carried out during this first night under the cloak of normal logistic resupply. 1st Line units would come back to the 2nd Line dumps and fill up with enough to bring their units to full stocks and ground-dump additional amounts beside weapon systems, ready for the flurry of activity prior to the abandonment of the position. This would go some way to help clear the 2nd Line stocks. 2nd Line transport could move some of what remained with it back to the new position under the guise of returning to fill up from 3rd Line stocks. Lastly on this night, 3rd Line transport need not travel to the division at all but would just dump the stocks it had brought forward on to the new position. These could be handed over to the division's advance parties and form the basis of the future 2nd Line dumps. Early in the second night, because the wheeled vehicles of logistic units will move faster than the tracks of combat units, the bulk of the division's logistic units would withdraw directly behind the new defensive position. Only the transport commander's immediate reserve might pause on any intermediate positions, in case their ammunition was needed to meet the unexpected.

Support for the delaying force could be provided by a mobile reserve of ammunition vehicles and a generous allocation of ambulances and casualty evacuation helicopters; in a withdrawal there will little chance of return trips. These would be grouped directly under the command of the delaying brigade's headquarters because, in a fast-moving delaying operation, this will be the only headquarters to have an up-to-date picture of what is happening on the battlefield. The divisional transport on its way back to the main defensive position would probably dump artillery ammunition on the likely intermediate gun positions for the support of the delaying force. There is the danger that the ammunition so dumped will be lost and in dumping the ammunition the location of the likely intermediate defensive positions will be given away. But this risk often has to be taken and can be reduced by careful siting of the dumps.

Logistic support for the new defensive position comes in two parts; the preparatory dumping of mines and defensive stores and the replenishment of the withdrawing force, especially the delaying brigade, when it gets back. The delaying brigade may have been so badly handled by the enemy that routine replenishment is not enough. In this case the delaying brigade would undertake the regeneration process known as reconstitution, which is worthy of a chapter in itself and has been given one in this book. If things go well, the division's logistic units, which left first, will have been able to reach and occupy their new working sites and be open for business by the time the combat troops get back. If this is not possible, some of the 2nd Line logistic assets of another formation could be used or 3rd Line assets deployed forward.

10.

Logistic Support for Transitional Operations

While there may only be the three pure phases of war, there are many other types of military operation that do not fall into the neat pigeon holes of Defensive, Delaying and Offensive operations. Clearly there will be operations that act as links between, or precursors to, the main phases of war. NATO calls these 'Transitional Operations'. As might be imagined, because this type of operation is not so clear-cut and tidy, they create additional challenges for the logistician.

Advance to Contact

'Mobility is the true test of a supply system.'[1]

The term 'Advance to Contact' describes the movement of a military force which, for the moment, has no real idea of the location of the enemy. In military terms, contact has been lost with the enemy. An Advance to Contact could be a cautious, stealthy affair, or it might be the all-out rush of a Patton-like sweep across France 1944. The operation ends when contact is made with a substantial body of the enemy who offer battle. For the logistician, this transitional operation means movement, and movement means that few logistic units can do productive work.

The extremes of this type of operation are such that on the one hand there could be no contact with the enemy, and thus no off-take other than fuel from the available logistic resources, or, on the other hand the intensity of a short-lived violent contact with the opposing forces. Such is the time factor of logistics that, if special arrangements have not already been made, there is little the logistician can do to influence main events. Reliance has to be placed on the combat units' own logistic assets, reinforced perhaps with fuel tankers from 2nd Line. If substantial logistic resupply is needed, the operation has stopped being an advance to contact and has become a 'Meeting Engagement'.

With the exception of fuel resupply, casualty evacuation would probably be the main logistic preoccupation in the Advance to Contact. The off-take of supplies against light opposition is unlikely to make the supply commander's life difficult. The maintenance commander can leave any vehicle casualties to be recovered later, for in the Advance to Contact the battlefield and its vital abandoned vehicles is the prize of the side that is advancing. The evacuation problem stems not from a shortage of medical facilities but from a reluctance on the part of the medical commander to open them for business. Once opened, they will become 'fixed' as casualties arrive and could end up too far away from the advancing troops they are supposed to support. The evacuation solution is either the ubiquitous helicopter or a very careful positioning of medical facilities along the route of the advance. The first would not be set up for business until the advance had moved off for about 50km. Over this distance casualties could easily be evacuated back to those dressing stations already set up and treating casualties. Casualties in the Advance to Contact can be expected to be lighter than those for the assault on an enemy main position so medical commanders could risk deploying their weakest assets first. Indeed, just for this transitional operation a commander might try to split a medical facility. Customarily this is not done. Administrative assets within the medical units are not scaled to be split but the light casualties traditionally experienced in an advance might mean that this risk could be taken.

All the logistic commanders face similar, if less stark, problems and they all stem from movement. During this movement, the logistic assets of the formation involved have to be 'balanced'. This is a military phrase and means that, while some units are moving, others are not, and are therefore open for logistic business. Thus the logistician 'leapfrogs' logistic units. The temporarily static logistic units may not necessarily work from their short-term site. Much will depend on the off-take of stocks, which in turn will result from the type and scale of opposition experienced by the combat troops. More usually, the logistic unit will pull off the road into a location that would be suitable as an operating base if needs be, and park up under cover awaiting the call forward to the next location. Customarily, the logistic units of an army are structured to carry out this sort of manoeuvre and, more often than not, each logistic unit will have three sub-units. Thus two could be moving while one waits, parked up. The urge to keep the logistic units as close to their combat colleagues as possible has to be weighed against the road congestion that would result and the vulnerability of logistic units to enemy action.

Like combat units, logistic units move by bounds. For combat units these bounds are tactical and relate to the next hilltop or valley. Logistic units move by bounds governed by a number of factors which interrelate to produce the next area where the logistic units will set up to operate. The prime factor is that the logistic units must be able to work from its chosen location, which implies a town or collection of villages to provide the overhead cover and road network needed for intensive logistic operations. Wooded areas can be used, especially if they are going to be occupied only for a short time. But if they are to be used intensively for a long period then the woodland tracks and rides will soon break up under the constant pounding of heavily laden cargo vehicles, and considerable engineering effort would have to be diverted from other tasks to keep them open. Other factors relate to distances from the existing or future sites for the 3rd Line logistic units and whether the nearest of those sites will be more than a night's drive away from the 2nd Line units' new location. Ideally they should not be separated by more than a night's drive. Another consideration stems from geomorphic factors. Logistic units are largely tied to the existing road network. Rivers, defiles and mountains all create choke points which enemy action can close down completely. If this were to happen when the logistic units were on the side of the obstacle away from the combat troops, logistic resupply and casualty evacuation would be stopped, apart from the little assistance that helicopters might provide. So, given an obstacle, logistic units would wish to be sited forward of it. In that way they can guarantee continued support to their combat units for those few days more that their own stocks would guarantee.

The transport commander in a formation about to advance to contact faces two specific challenges. The first of these relates to fuel. History abounds with examples of offensives that were halted or reduced in effect because they ran into fuel problems. Patton's great 1944 drive from Brittany to the Rhine is one of the more famous of these. Part of Patton's problem stemmed from the fact that fuel was in short supply; not enough could be landed in Europe from England. But another part of the fuel problem was one of distribution and this problem remains today. The difficulty is not that there is not enough fuel, but that it cannot be moved quickly enough from where it is to where it will be needed.

Patton, at least, was helped by another of the axioms of the Advance to Contact – that ammunition is used to a lesser degree than in all other operations of war. Patton's logistic commanders could load ammunition vehicles with jerrycans of fuel. This option is rarely open to a modern-day logistic commander. The growth of bulk refuelling has meant a growth in specialised road fuel tankers, matching in turn to the growth in the rate of fuel consumption of modern military fighting vehicles. Thus the number of jerrycans required to support an advance would be difficult to cobble together. It is the road tanker that has to shoulder the bulk of this particular load. There are disadvantages to the tanker in this role: there are not a lot of them; they are vulnerable to enemy action; and their low mobility ties them to roads that might be open. There will be an increasing turn-round problem as the advance puts the sources of supply further away. The problem is almost insoluble, albeit only short term. 3rd Line tankers can be moved further forward and placed under 2nd Line control, and 2nd Line tankers can be placed under the command of combat units who would have started the Advance to Contact with full tanks. But the availability and distribution of fuel will remain a nagging worry to both the combat and the logistic commanders. In such a situation a Red Army commander would call upon one of the pipeline brigades from Front. Laying at a planned, but very optimistic, rate of 30km per day, the pipeline would be unlikely to keep up with the rate of advance. But every kilometre covered by the pipeline reduces the turn-round time of 2nd and 3nd Line fuel tankers back to the pipehead or storage site. No NATO nation has such a brigade. The British have a reserve pipeline, but it is only 80km long at the most and it certainly cannot be laid as fast as the one constructed by the Red Army. Consequently, a NATO army will have to rely on road tankers collecting fuel from the nearest storage site.

The transport commander's second problem will be his overall turn-round times. As the advance continues and the sources of supply get further away, the turn-round times for all transport vehicles will increase. There is a real chance that, if the Advance to Contact turns into something more serious, the combat units might use up stocks quicker than the transport commander can replenish them. This is largely because so much of the 2nd Line stocks cannot be carried on wheels and has to be dumped on the ground. The remedy for this is for the 3rd Line to take over the 2nd Line dumps and for the vehicles that would have been used to in-load the new 3rd Line dumps to move direct to the proposed 2nd Line dumps and off-load there. While this co-operation is eminently sensible from the 2nd Line transport commander's point of view, it is less so to the eyes of his 3rd Line comrade. 2nd Line dumps might not be configured for 3rd Line working and, during a hurried takeover in the middle of the night, the 2nd Line soldiers will probably get rid of all their 'deficiencies' on the incoming 3rd Line troops. A dump sufficient for a division might not be large enough to hold all the eventual stocks of the 3rd Line unit that would be the new owners of the site. Furthermore, the turn-round problem would not have disappeared, but only been transferred from 2nd to 3rd Line. It would be the 3rd Line commander that saw a decrease in his task vehicle efficiency as they had further to go. Interestingly, such co-operation seems to be offered willingly in peacetime map exercises but, historically, seems to have been much more difficult to achieve once operations start.

All the logistic commanders would really only have just the one eye on the support for the Advance to Contact; because of the time factor in logistics the other eye would be firmly focused on the next operation to take place. Thus, in the Advance to Contact, the logistician would reinforce unit logistic assets in order to increase their capacity to meet the unexpected and to ensure that a logistic want resulting from a small-scale engagement should not hold up the advance. However, his main logistic attention and effort would be devoted to preparation for the next phase of the operation and the movement of 2nd Line and 3rd Line logistic units, during the logistically 'quiet' phase that the Advance to Contact represents, to better positions for subsequent operations.

Meeting Engagements

It sounds rather simplistic and self-evident but a meeting engagement can best be described as an engagement that takes place between two opponents that have been moving. Inherent in this definition is that neither of the protagonists is deeply entrenched; although wise soldiers of any army entrench at the least opportunity. The Meeting Engagement is essentially a battle of manoeuvre. The action is sometimes deliberately brought about as one side believes its advantage lies in fighting this sort of battle, rather than assault a prepared defensive position. Both the Wehrmacht and the Red Army favoured this sort of engagement. Sometimes the action is just a means to an end; fought on the way to attaining some greater objective. It is vital that the logistic commander knows which of these battles his operational commander intends to fight because the logistic plan stems directly from the tactical one.

Whichever engagement is the aim of the operational commander, the logistic commanders face the inherent difficulty for a logistician in a battle of manoeuvre: almost all logistic units need to be a stationary and settled if they are to achieve their best work rates. Unfortunately, a stationary logistic unit in a fluid Meeting Engagement is a vulnerable beast. Supply dumps can easily be overrun and surprised repair units are likely to have to abandon the vehicle casualties on which they are working. Furthermore, the battle might move away from the logistic units and they would have to expend the effort and, more importantly the time, to pack up and follow the action. Consequently, if the operational commander's aim is to bring the enemy to battle, the 2nd Line logistic commander would probably deploy two-thirds of his available assets and open them for business. One third would be held in reserve and at least one supply dump would start to be filled up. The bulk of the transport assets would not be able to move forward until the battle is won, which could take not less than four hours for a brigade level engagement. In this four hours, part of the available transport fleet could dump its stocks and be well on its way back to the 3rd Line dumps to replenish.

If it is the operational commander's intention to move on quickly, or to avoid battle, the 2nd Line logistic commander will deploy only the barest minimum. Because of the likely intensity of the Meeting Engagement, it would be unwise to deploy nothing; but opening one third of the logistic units for business will buy time for a better assessment to be made. This third could well handle the immediate logistic requirement which, if the battle seems likely to go on, could be reinforced by the opening of a further third.

Link-up Operations and Isolated Operations

NATO treats the transitional Link-up and Isolated operations as separate and, for the logistician, they do present starkly different challenges. The logistican supporting the link-up force has the traditional problem of distribution. The logistician with the isolated force has the very different problem of a shortage of stocks to be distributed. The fact that NATO lists these transitional operations is a welcome reflection of German Second World War experience. On the Eastern Front, with its great scales of distances and numbers, such operations became very much routine, especially from 1943 to 1945. It was the expected scale and intensity of a likely Russian assault in post-war Europe that forced Western armies to study the difficulties of being cut off for considerable periods of time.

Link-Up Operations

Link-Up Operations are those which take place when an army attempts to regain contact, and especially logistic resupply, with an element that has been cut off by enemy action. The priority is to open up a communications corridor through which resupply can flow. The difficulties for the logistician are that really two operations have to be supported at once. The first is the logistic support of the combat troops attempting to break through to the encircled force. For this support the logistic posture is very much that for the Attack or Advance to Contact. Conversely, once contact with the encircled troops is made, the priority goes to moving enough supplies for them to continue in action or to be withdrawn to undertake Reconstitution. Thus, behind the combat troops battling to regain contact with their cut-off comrades, lie the makings of an incredible traffic jam as combat units, logistic units supporting them, the engineers waiting to clear the route for logistic traffic and the logistic convoys waiting to rush resupply through to the encircled forces all jostle for road space and bicker over the limited routes available. Perhaps this is the reason why all the great modern captains have also been described as great traffic policemen.

Like most things in logistics, the remedy is simple in concept but very difficult in execution. If resources allow, the best thing is to separate the two elements. The resupply columns will be found from those 3rd Line logistic units that would have been supporting the cut-off force and would be made up largely of ambulances (there is likely to have been little casualty evacuation from the pocket) and resupply vehicles loaded with the necessary priority supplies and fuel signalled-in by the cut-off force. There is little these columns can do to help the break-through battle. Their presence close to the battle would hinder things as they use road space and valuable real estate. Thus these units would be held ready loaded in hides as much as 30 km behind the action.

The units supporting the break-through deploy and operate as normal but have to accept that, once link-up is achieved, priority on the link-up route will be given to transport assets moving to replenish the cut-off force. If needs be, the link-up force has to live off its existing stocks and resupply itself only by those tracks and cross-country routes which would not affect the flow along the route to the encircled force. This is risky for the break-in force as, having fought hard to achieve the link-up, it then needs its own replenishment. However, the needs of the encircled force will be much greater.

The link-up operation requires great co-operation between the logistic commanders concerned. The priority of them all will be the treatment and evacuation of the casualties of the encircled force. Time will be of the essence. Instead of just relying on evacuation to 3rd Line hospitals, the medical assets of the break-in force could be reinforced so that the cut-off force's casualties can be treated as soon as possible. An even better solution, if the operational situation allowed, would be to move a 3rd Line field hospital forward and keep it ready for the cut-off force's casualties.

Isolated Operations

Second World War Eastern Front examples of the isolated operations of complete corps, and even armies, abound. Western Europeans, used to relatively cramped geography and limited numbers compared with the campaign in Russia, find such examples difficult to comprehend. But, even in the West, there are some examples (such as the US defence of Bastogne in the 1944 Battle of the Bulge) which although smaller, show that such operations are not just limited to the vast distances and huge numbers of Eastern Europe and European Russia.

The encircled force has unusual logistic problems. From a normal situation where commanders have enough logistic resources, but worry about whether the supplies can be distributed in time to match combat unit consumption, the commander now faces a situation where there will be no resupply whatsoever and the encircled force has to live off the stocks it held before it became isolated. Depending on the size of the force, these stocks could be considerable. A division, for example, could have stocks sufficient for up to five days of intensive operations.

The operational commander, who now has to face a combat threat from 360 degrees, also has to add as one of his prime concerns – logistics. Immediately the force becomes isolated the operational commander has to enforce some form of rationing. Again, like most things in logistics, this is simple in concept but difficult in execution. The first priority is to establish just what stocks are held by the force. The staff of Paulus's German 6th Army cut off at Stalingrad started such a stock-take immediately their force became encircled. Their aim was to establish whether the encircled 6th Army possessed enough fuel to be able to supply a break-out attempt to link up with the forces striving to reach them. Based on the returns from formations and units, they had to inform Paulus that, even with rationing, the 6th Army did not have enough fuel. Reluctantly, Paulus had to abandon the idea of a break out and was forced to wait for relief to come to him. Immediate post-war US Army historical researchers spotted the anomaly that, despite the pessimistic estimates of fuel stocks given by units to the staff, the 6th Army had been able to keep on fighting for months after they should have run out of fuel. Records of the very small amounts flown in while airstrips remained open in the pocket were not sufficient to match the consumption that had obviously taken place. They interviewed Paulus's logistic staff and unit quartermasters and established that the staff of almost every unit and formation had deliberately concealed the true size of their fuel holdings. They feared that, if they declared their true stocks, some of this fuel would be taken from them and given to others. Thus, while it is obvious that all stocks in an encircled formation should be put under central control, the 6th Army example shows that this is more easily said than done.

The logistic commander of the encircled force faces two particular problems, casualty evacuation and treatment and fuel resupply. The rations for men can be reduced and they will continue to fight, especially if well led and motivated. Artillery gunners can be rationed. Interestingly, rationing gunners does not seem to have the great operational effect one might suspect. Gunners will fire ammunition if they have it. If they have shortages they will use what they have on the highest scoring and priority targets. This goes some way to support the truism that:

> The higher the level one goes, it is not the number of artillery tubes that counts, but the number of rounds available to fire from those tubes.

German experience was that subordinate operational commanders and artillery units were not to be trusted. If they were given a day's worth of ammunition and told to use only a half, they would use the lot. Consequently, the German practice was to give units only their ration, and no more.

Machines are not like men. Exhortation, example and leadership have no effect on them. Consequently, fuel becomes an overriding concern for logistic commanders in isolated operations. Because fuel consumption breaks into fuel for automotive vehicles and fuel for static running engines, economies can be made immediately in static consumption rates. This recourse is, however, difficult for a modern army where generators power air defence radars and communication nets as well as headquarters' lighting sets and workshop heaters. Armoured fighting vehicle movement has to be restricted to the bare minimum and traffic limited as much as possible to wheeled vehicles, whose consumption rates are low. The isolated force has to become a scavanger for fuel. Every soldier should be equipped with plastic and rubber tubing for siphoning fuel from abandoned vehicles and captured enemy stocks. Fuel can be air-dropped or, more efficiently, air-landed to the isolated force, provided the air superiority situation allows. Above all, the priority for fuel issues has to go to those combat units involved in the link-up attempt.

An isolated formation that remains static withers on the vine. Consequently, the operational commander will want to move his force towards the nearest friendly units or the formation that is going to make the link-up attempt. To support this movement the logistic commander has to adopt the concept of 'caterpillar' movement. Because there is no resupply for the isolated force, any stocks it has become precious and too vital to abandon. Thus dumps and other static sites have to be moved as close as possible to direction of movement, and then moved again as the break out continues.

The treatment and evacuation of casualties is rather more difficult for the logistic commander of the isolated force. To caterpillar medical installations would mean the death of casualties too sick to move. Conversely, the abandonment of these casualties to the uncertain care of the enemy will harm the morale of the isolated force. The problem can be partly avoided if casualties are taken to the medical unit nearest to the direction of the break-out. At least these casualties will have some time to recover before the unit has to move. But, inevitably, some casualties may have to be abandoned to the enemy. If the situation allows air evacuation, then clearly the priority goes to casualties and to the useless mouths of the force; that is, logistic units whose stocks have been exhausted and combat troops whose equipment has been destroyed, damaged beyond quick repair or which can no longer be supported.

Relief in Place

The remaining three Transitional Operations present greater problems to the operational commander than they do to the logistician. All, however, hinge around a successful control of movement because all involve the units of two formations occupying the same real estate at the same time; often a recipe for confusion and military disaster.

The relief in place involves one formation taking over the battle from another by taking over the positions occupied by the force to be relieved. The logistic task is relatively simple. The stocks of the force to be relieved are left *in situ* and taken over by the relieving force, who, as they arrive, will bring more. The only problem is likely to be squabbling among the supply commanders over the accounts and just how much is being handed over. Similarly, care for those casualties of the engaged force that cannot be moved will be assumed by the incoming medical units. The repair units will treat damaged vehicles in a similar way.

The very movement of all these logistic units could give the relief away to the enemy. It can be hidden, however, if the night before the relief is used for logistic advance parties to join the engaged force to take over its stocks. On the night of the relief the relieving logistic units move forward instead of the normal resupply columns, thus masking somewhat the increased logistic traffic. The relieved force returns in the place of what would have been the empty 3rd Line vehicles returning to their base in the corps area.

Forward Passage of Lines

The Forward Passage of Lines involves the movement of one military force through another. It assumes that contact has been made with the enemy and thus that the force moving through will be in combat once it has moved past its own troops in contact. The logistic commander of the moving force will be looking for considerable help from the logistic units of the engaged force for the first part of the operation. Given some reinforcement from the logistic units of the moving force, it is these units that could provide medical and repair support to the moving force for up to 30 km beyond the existing positions. This would mean the moving force would not have to deploy and would start with all its logistic assets mobile and uncommitted. The existing forces' units will, however, be unlikely to release transport assets to support the moving force. Their vehicles will be supporting their own combat units, still in contact with the enemy. It may be, however, that the engaged force's supply dumps could be made available to the moving force, thus reducing the turn-round time for those vehicles that would otherwise have to return the long distance to the 3rd Line dumps.

Rearward Passage of Lines

The Rearward Passage of Lines takes place when one force withdraws through another. Thus the withdrawing force is in contact with the enemy and logistic support for it has to be guaranteed until it has retired behind friendly lines. Security considerations are important for this operation because the premature movement of logistic traffic could alert the enemy to the fact that the rearward movement is to take place.

Again, co-operation between the logistic commanders of the withdrawing force and the in-situ force is essential. The in-situ force is not in contact and its logistic units would largely be free, and thus able, to help the withdrawing force. The night before the operation is to take place, under the cover of the guise of nightly resupply traffic, elements of the withdrawing force could move to the area of the in-situ force to reinforce its logistic units. There is always a temptation to move the withdrawing force's logistic units the night before the operation takes place. Apart from the security considerations, this is unwise because the unexpected will always occur and those logistic units sent to the rear would probably be just the ones it is found were needed. Furthermore, the locations of logistic units are to the rear of the combat units. Being completely wheeled, the movement of logistic units is faster. On the night of the rearward movement, there is no bar to all the combat and logistic units of the withdrawing formation starting to move at the same time. The logistic units should be through the inevitable choke points before the combat units arrive.

During this night-time movement, and the afternoon of that day, personnel and vehicle casualties would be lifted back to the logistic units of the in-situ force.

11.

Reconstitution

The basis for NATO's definition of what is a transitional operation stems from the criterion that such operations link up or precede the three main phases of war. Yet one operation that is likely to be the precursor of almost any military operation is not listed as a transitional operation. All armies at some time or other will have to face the task of taking a formation or unit that has been savagely mauled by the enemy and getting it ready for battle again. Such an operation is called 'Reconstitution' and is clearly a preliminary to any subsequent operations and thus should really be listed as a transitional operation. Unfortunately, it is not. At the corps level and above, the operational level in military-speak, the reconstitution of a battered formation is one of the few ways open to commanders to achieve some form of force regeneration. It is probably the only way that commanders will be able to generate effective reserves, for it is unlikely that Western commanders of the future will have massive reserves on which to draw.

Interestingly, although reconstitution will have to be carried out by every army, it is the least discussed and the least practised; with the honourable exception of the US Army who have actually exercised at it. In some armies, peacetime command post exercises (those without troops and just the commanders and their staffs) abound with units that have been reduced to 60 per cent strength being hurled back into action the next day. Yet history is full of examples that show that to do this is military suicide and that the knocked-about unit, no matter what its paper effectiveness, will be useless unless given time to recover and reform.

One Historical Example

Perhaps one of the most clear cut examples is the Ardennes experience of the American 28th Infantry Division in late 1944. An American unit is used as the example, not because American units are more prone to this sort of thing than those of other armies, but because American historical analysis is the most intensive, honest and best documented. Other armies have suffered similar problems; but regimental and national pride often clouds the picture.

By late 1944 the 28th US Infantry Division was a very experienced formation indeed. It had landed in Normandy, fought there, and in the subsequent push across France. In November 1944, the division formed part of the V US Corps, as part of the 1st US Army, and its task was to fight through the

Huertgen Wald some 15 km south-east of Aachen and take the town of Schmidt. Eight days later the divisional commander, General Cota, had to ask for his division to be withdrawn from combat. It was withdrawn and then put back in the line – just in time to meet the Germans Ardennes offensive. Indeed, based on the division's earlier combat performance, German intelligence had picked on the 28th Division's area of the American defensive line as the spot that should form the point of main effort for their forces on that part of the front.

To the Germans' surprise, the division fought extremely well and, although eventually succumbing to the mass that faced them, their defence fatally delayed the German attack timetable and isolated parts of the division (including the divisional commander and his headquarters company) were still fighting three days after the offensive started. Clearly, something had happened to the division in the two short weeks between the Huertgen Wald debacle and their valiant efforts in the Battle of the Bulge. They had, in fact, undergone the process now called reconstitution. Before looking more closely at just what, reconstitution is and how it works, it might be best to spend some time analysing just why the 28th Division's Huertgen Wald performance was so poor. By doing so, the reason for some of the constituent parts of reconstitution can be better explained.

The Americans practised a continuous combat casualty replacement system. Thus a wounded soldier was replaced immediately by another; equipment was treated similarly. This system meant that the division was kept at something like its full strength at all times; although, as an aside, no army unit has ever actually been at full strength – there are too many minor accidents, ailments and detachments to allow this to happen. During periods of relatively light casualties, this system worked well. The small number of raw replacements could be taken under the wing of the more experienced until they were fully fit to take their place in the line.

The rifle, or combat infantryman, part of the division's 14,000 strength was about 6,000. During its six days in the Huertgen Wald the 28th Division had just over 5,000 casualties, the bulk of them riflemen. Almost everyone in its front line combat strength had had to be replaced. The figures for the vital sub-unit commanders and NCOs were no better. In the 28th Division's assault on Schmidt, the bulk of the rifle strength of the division was lost, either to enemy action or to complaints arising from the atrocious weather and terrain conditions. The division reeled back from the assault with roughly the same numbers of soldiers it had taken in. But it was clear that the division had not had enough time to assimilate all these reinforcements; hence the debacle.

Reconstitution Timetable

All Second World War armies practised reconstitution in some form or other. The Wehrmacht was particularly effective at this. All were forced to

1st Day - Units were left alone to sleep and talk about their experiences. Military discipline was relaxed.
2nd Day - Baths were provided, hair was cut, equipment issued and replacements started to arrive. Military discipline was re-imposed.
3rd Day - Platoon level training.
4th Day - Company level training.
5th and 6th Days - Battalion level training.
7th, 8th and 9th Days - Brigade level training.
10th Day - Unit and formation declared operationally effective.

FIG. 11.1 Second World War brigade reconstitution timetable

recognise that a unit at 100 per cent strength is not necessarily a 100 per cent effective unit. Clearly it took time to assimilate reinforcements and for an equipment-intensive armoured unit or formation a longer period was needed. In the end armies adopted the almost template reconstitution timetable shown in Figure 11.1.

It is argued that such a lengthy time period for reconstitution cannot be allowed to modern armies; especially those of the Western powers, who need every soldier they have in the line. But such an attitude is very short-sighted indeed. Historical example shows that it is folly to fill a unit with replacement men and equipment, and then to expect them to be immediately effective; the 28th Division at Schmidt should be example enough. There are, however, some ways in which the reconstitution process can be speeded up and all, in some way, involve the logistician.

The Commander's Options for Reconstitution

When considering a battered unit or formation a commander has a number of options open to him. The unit can reorganise. Within the unit, equipment and men can be moved to make two good companies out of three battered ones. At the level of platoon, this reorganisation has to be carried out after every action. Platoon commanders reallocate men and ammunition to fill the gaps caused by every assault. But there is a limit to the number of times such quick reorganisations can take place. Operational effectiveness drops the more they are carried out. Furthermore, to reorganise companies is a significant decision and has far-reaching consequences. A brigade commander would certainly wish to know that a battalion commander intended forming three companies into two.

The commander may wish to break the unit up completely and use its companies and platoons to fill the gaps in other units' ranks 'redistribution'. Clearly this would be a very undesirable option from a commander's point of view. Once broken up the unit will be difficult to reform, if it can be done at all. The commander has to balance the merits of keeping a much reduced unit in the field, its relative operational ineffectiveness and the costs in command, control and logistic assets of keeping it independent. He would lose a number of 'points of command' and may prefer to keep a seriously under-strength unit in the line, and use it for tasks suitable for its reduced strength. The unit, too, would now be a veteran one and its operational effectiveness might be greater than its mere numbers might seem to show. Lastly, in armies with a strongly defined 'regimental system', the veterans of a broken-up unit might not easily be assimilated by another. The British Army Second World War Salerno mutiny by 192 soldiers had its roots, in part, in that the returning veterans of the 50th Tyne & Tees and the 51st Highland Divisions had been told that they were not to return to their own formations but were to be allocated as replacements to other divisions.

But most commanders would wish to make the unit or formation as it was before. This 'regeneration' process is the most time-consuming of all the reconstitution methods; there will be considerable movement of men, stocks and new equipments and it will involve an intensive and lengthy training bill. To further complicate matters, time might be so pressing that the commander decides to reorganise one unit, redistribute the second, and regenerate the third!

Reconstitution Decisions

Before the logistic actions of reconstitution can start, a number of decisions have, therefore, to be made. The first of these is perhaps the most important; it governs all the others. This is the question of time. Just how much time is available for the reconstitution process? Intelligence staffs will advise, but the commander has to weigh this advice. The eventual amount of time allocated is a result of the commander's judgement as to the immediacy of the enemy threat, and therefore how long he can afford to have a formation out of the line, versus how long his experience tells him the formation concerned will need to take in its reinforcements of men and matériel and then be fit for action.

The time factor will govern which type of reconstitution, or mix, is to be carried out. If time is short then it is unlikely that the formation can undergo regeneration. Some mix of reorganisation and redistribution would probably be all that could be attempted in the time available. Conversely, if intelligence tells the commander that the enemy attacks are due to run out of steam-because they are outstripping their supplies, regeneration could well be considered.

A commander has to decide what unit types are his priority for reconstitution–tank or infantry? This will depend on the next mission that he has in mind for the formation. If it is to act as a mobile reserve and counter-attack force then priority will be given to getting the tank units ready. If the next mission is one of defence or the commander wants an airmobile reserve, then reconstitution priority will go to the infantry.

If the time element is so pressing that the commander needs something, anything, as soon as possible, then he might order that priority should go to the 'strongest first', which would ensure that at least one unit or formation was ready swiftly. But this would mean the reconstitution of the remainder took longer. All logistic attention would be concentrated on the first unit and there would be little concurrent activity to support the others.

In armies that do not have permanently configured tank/infantry units but which practise 'grouping' (where tank or infantry battalions exchange companies to meet the requirement for a particular operation), the questions is whether the reconstitution is be carried out by the tactical grouping or are the detached companies to return to their parent battalions? The answer can have a significant effect on the time taken. On the one hand, it is easier and quicker if units are all of the same type: it reduces the number of points to which replacement personnel, stocks and equipment have to be sent. It is always a good idea in war to keep things simple. On the other hand, time is taken by the sub-units to return to their parent battalions and then, reconstitution completed, to move to the tactical grouping they are joining for subsequent operations. On balance, most armies prefer to reconstitute by parent unit; what the British army calls by 'cap-badge'.

This list of questions shows that, while the actual execution of reconstitution is very much a logistic function, the decisions which govern how it is to be carried out are very much for operational commanders.

The Reconstitution Area

The areas for reconstitution need careful selection. They have to be relatively far back, at least out of all enemy artillery range, and they need certain facilities. They must be sited near to, but off, a main supply route. 'Near to', because the units will use this route themselves and so will their replacement personnel, stocks and equipment; 'but off', because this route cannot be blocked by such traffic as it is needed for the support of the forces still engaged with the enemy. The infrastructure (roads, hardstanding for work-shops, cover for the logistic units and for the returning combat units) will be needed to support the reconstitution process and air defence cover and reasonable access to an area suitable for training. It would be helpful if the area had a railhead which could bring in replacements, especially of heavy equipment, and take away casualties. Such areas are not easy to find but an

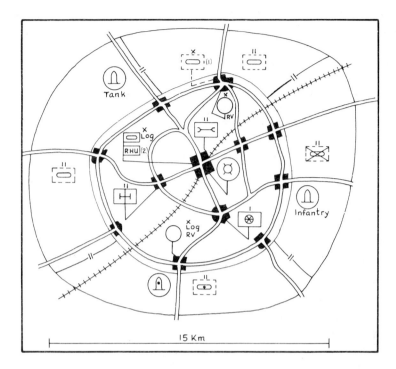

1. Future location for the brigade
headquarters. It should be almost
the last unit to arrive.

2. Reinforcement Holding Unit.

3. Specialised troops such as
aviation and air defence reconstitute
with their parent unit and not
with the brigade.

FIG. 11.2 Idealised armoured brigade reconstitution area

ideal one, for an armoured brigade, might look like that shown in Figure
11.2.

The Sources for Replacement Men and Materiel

Recent conflicts seem to show that the intensity of warfare is hotting up.
The Arab/Israeli wars produced considerable daily casualties, especially of
equipment. Modern weapons are even more accurate than before and the
potential great clash of armoured and highly mobile masses seems to show
that there will be heavy attrition in any modern high intensity conflict
between relatively balanced opponents. But the much preferred 'regeneration' type of reconstitution can only be attempted if the replacement re-

sources of men and equipment are available; hence most armies' large war reserve stockpiles and the importance placed on the mobilisation of reservists. The equipment could come from a number of sources and the Conference on Security and Confidence Building in Europe (CSE) observers (deployed to monitor tank and personnel holdings as part of mutual confidence-building measures) have found that all armies have sources of equipment other than the obvious war reserve stockpiles.

The first source is from what armies call their maintenance reserve. This is a reserve of complete equipments, including tanks, held ready to ensure units can continue training by replacing peacetime vehicle accident casualties or unit equipment that is undergoing a major and lengthy overhaul in a base workshop somewhere. The second source is from 'reconstitution packs'. These are packs held deliberately against a certain requirement for reconstitution to be carried out. Such packs are held by most of the front-line NATO corps to replace the inevitable losses in each corps' returning covering force. A third source is the normal resupply system. Complete equipments can normally be found wending their way up the supply chain and could be diverted (but at a cost to the unit for which it was intended) to the reconstituting force. If there are no complete equipments then the supply chain can often produce the bits and pieces that together might make one up. This is unlikely in the case of the very large equipments, like main battle tanks, but more likely in the smaller sub-systems. Lastly, there is the output of a nation's own industry and that of its allies. At any given time factories will be producing equipment or have equipment on hand awaiting delivery to customers; this is before the factories shift to full wartime production. British industry's response in times of crisis has been magnificent in this respect. The Falkland Islands campaign came at a particularly awkward time for one British air defence battalion. It was changing its 'mark' of Rapier anti-aircraft missile launchers for another and had not been equipped with its bad weather radars. The British Aircraft Corporation used a mixture of equipments already completed or nearing the end of its production line to take only 48 hours to bring the battalion up to full strength.[1] Fully equipped, the battalion was then deployed to the South Atlantic. Similarly, for the 1991 liberation of Kuwait, British industry rushed the Multi-Launcher Rocket System (MLRS), the Demountable Rack Off-loading and Pick-up System (DROPS) and many other equipments into service in time for the start of the ground offensive.

The provision of replacement equipment is, however, not a simple one. The bulk of the replacement equipment in most armies' war stockpiles is not the most modern. Given the length of time that armies keep main equipments in service – a main battle tank could last 25 years in front-line service – young regular soldiers may only ever have seen the latest tank type. The situation could arise where only reservists have experience of a tank type which comes out of the war reserve. Thus the most 'current' soldiers, the regulars, could have little experience of their replacement equipment and the reservists might find themselves manning a modern equipment of which they have no experience at all. All this, plus the requirement to 'bed-in' new commanders, highlights the need for there to be a training period after the mechanical logistic phase of reconstitution has been completed.

Clearly, in reconstitution, much depends on how long hostilities have been going on, and just what equipments and what reinforcements remain uncommitted. Lastly, the state of the reconstituting units should not be forgotten. They will have been living on their adrenalin for the time they have been in action. They will be dirty, thirsty, hungry and very, very tired. There is no guarantee that they will arrive in the reconstitution area in the neat order planned by the staff movement table. Companies will have been cut off and would have had to rejoin friendly lines via other points. Wounded and tired officers and soldiers will have lost their way. Companies might be commanded by junior captains and platoons by corporals. Some fighting vehicles will be untouched. Others will come back limping and some will break down along the way back. If ever a logistic operation of war should be simple, based on common sense and designed to make life easy for the combat soldier, then it is reconstitution.

PLATE 31 Logistic support across a beach. Shown here are a British Royal Fleet Auxiliary landing ship logistic and two ramp craft logistic (foreground) carrying logistic vehicles. (*A.C.D. Welch*)

PLATE 32 A Beach Petroleum site. Sea fuel tankers are vulnerable beasts. It is rarely safe to keep them stationed permanently off a beach-head. A Ship-to-Shore pipeline has to be laid and this site shows the land end of such a pipeline. (*A.C.D. Welch*)

PLATE 33 A British Army *MEXE* float. This equipment was invented to serve as a ship to shore lighter. It is sectionised, can be assembled in the Theatre of Operations and can be configured to match the loads to be carried. This photograph shows a *MEXE* afloat in San Carlos Water during the British Falkland Islands campaign. Originally designed as a calm water lighter, the seas on this photograph do not look placid. The author checked. This *MEXE* float and its load made it safely to shore. (*A.C.D. Welch*)

PLATE 34   A British Army *EAGER BEAVER* rough terrain fork lift truck after an air drop. The *EAGER BEAVER* is a rough terrain fork lift truck and is dropped early in a parachute operation in order that it can help clear the Drop Zone quickly. (*M. Kerley*)

PLATE 35 A water convoy in the Saudi-Arabian desert. In this case, British Army *DROPS* vehicles with their flat racks fitted with water tanks for the support of the British 1st Armoured Division during the Liberation of Kuwait 1991. (*A. Taylor*)

PLATE 36 A fuel tanker convoy in the snows of Norway. Mountain warfare still needs fuel in appreciable quantities. Even static armies need fuel to power generators and to provide heating. Low gear mountain driving increases this consumption. (*A.C.D. Welch*)

PLATE 37 Royal Navy *SEA KING* helicopter. The helicopter is particularly important in special climates and terrain. Here ammunition is being lifted to the British Commando Logistic Regiment Royal Marines' brigade logistic area. Because specialised brigades are relatively light logistic consumers, helicopters can play a much more significant part in their resupply. But in snow, helicopter pilots fear *Whiteout*, when snow conditions make it difficult to tell where the air ends and the surface of the ground begins. This rather 'grey' photograph was taken in relatively 'good' visibility conditions for the Arctic. (*A.C.D. Welch*)

PLATE 38 A *BV 206* oversnow vehicle. To travel over snow successfully needs vehicles with a low ground pressure. The Swedish *BV 206* is in service with a number of armies, including the British, as an infantry and mortar carrier as well as a logistic resupply vehicle. Such vehicles are often as useful in marsh and swamp as they are in snow. (*Author*)

PLATE 39 A British Army *SUPACAT* airmobile all-terrain vehicle. Once landed airmobile troops are limited, like their parachute comrades, to the speed of the foot infantryman. Small, light-weight vehicles can prove invaluable as weapon carrier, casualty evacuation and logistic resupply vehicles. The *SUPACAT* is one such and, in addition to being airmobile, is also amphibious. (*H Bentley-Marchant*)

PLATE 40   A German Army *CH 53* medium transport helicopter. Few current helicopters can lift great loads. The introduction of a type that was truly 'Heavy Lift' could revolutionise logistics as the attack helicopter has revolutionised tactics. In this photograph the load is being carried internally. Helicopter crews dislike carrying internal loads and much prefer them to be underslung. Loading internally takes time. This makes the helicopter vulnerable on the ground for longer periods and uses up fuel that could be being used to travel distance. Besides, the load chief and the crew have to tie down the load and secure it themselves! (*H.G. Ziegler*)

PLATE 41   Parachute resupply. Although modern warfare might preclude parachute operations of Second World War size, intervention operations in up to brigade strength are possible and will need to be resupplied. There are many other, more conventional, military operations when an air drop could mean the difference between success and failure. Moreover, parachute supply can help in famine and disaster relief and thus it is a technique that armies would do well to maintain. (*H Bentley-Marchant*)

PLATE 42   Class X supply operations. The nicest supply task of all. In this case, aid to the Kurds in Northern Iraq 1991 by the Commando Logistic Regiment Royal Marines. (*RAOC Secretariat*)

12.

Logistic Support for Specialised Operations

History has shown that man will fight in almost any terrain and that, if an invention is made, more often than not man will use it in warfare. Each type of terrain and each type of invention brings with it its own particular challenges. Fortunately for the logistician, it is rare that these special circumstances change the general principles of logistics or, indeed, most of the logistic world's way of operation. Each different type of terrain or way of waging war does, however, highlight particular facets or functions of logistics and reduce the importance of others.

Amphibious Operations

Armies have been landing from the sea since antiquity and the logistic problems created by amphibious operations are well known. For the logistician, an amphibious operation breaks down into two distinct phases: support for the force on the beach and support for this force once it moves inland.

Support for the force on the beach will present little problem if air superiority is held. The vessels at sea serve as floating depots and, provided the contents were stowed for landing and not stowed to maximise shipping space, resupply can easily be moved by landing craft or helicopter to the landing force. Furthermore, the fire support for the landing and the defence of the beach-head comes primarily from naval vessels and aircraft. As artillery ammunition represents the bulk of the logistic load for a conventional force this takes quite a strain off the logistic commander. This reduction is welcome for, until such time as the beach-head is widened enough to put the beach out of range of enemy artillery, any logistic stocks landed run the risk of being lost.

If air superiority is not held then the logistic situation changes drastically. The British landing force in the 1982 campaign to retake the Falkland Islands had been assured of air superiority. So the logistic plan was based on floating depots held in the shipping in San Carlos Bay. When Argentine air raids drove the shipping away, for all but the hours of darkness, the logistic plan had to be radically revised. If air superiority is lost, or is not held, then stocks have to built up on the shore from the start of the operation, and the risk taken that they might be lost; as were some of the ammunition stocks of the British 3rd Commando Brigade at San Carlos.

Having built up stocks ashore, logistic support for the landing force becomes much harder as the landing force moves inland off the beach. Two factors interrelate. The first is that amphibious landing forces are largely composed of infantry. Foot infantry's logistic requirements are relatively small and little transport is required to lift their needs. Conversely, the landing force is unlikely to have more transport than that it lands itself. Once the landing force moves out of range of naval gunfire support the problem is made worse by the need to resupply its integral artillery.

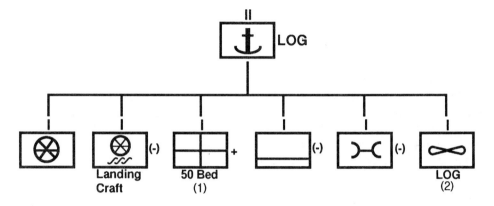

1.   The proximity of naval vessels with their medical facilities means the medical facility can be smaller than normal.

2.   Nowadays, a Marine brigade could be said to be as airmobile as any. Helicopters would play their part in resupply but no land aircraft workshop is really needed as they will be repaired on their helicopter carrier.

FIG. 12.1 An amphibious logistic battalion

The role of the helicopter is vital to a modern amphibious landing. Helicopters can fly direct from the ships to where the supplies are needed. In the casualty evacuation role they can have wounded to a fully-equipped operating theatre within 20 minutes. They cannot, however, replace other transport means. Bad weather can affect their performance or restrict all flying. Even when flying, a medium lift helicopter can carry about four tonnes. Heavier helicopters such as the US Chinook can lift only about eight tonnes. Thus helicopters cannot lift all that much. Even more importantly, helicopters may not take long to pick up their loads, but it takes a considerable effort and a degree of time (about 15 minutes depending on the space and number of hands involved) to prepare those loads. Unfortunately, there are not many helicopter landing points (areas where helicopters can land) on most vessels and this further restricts the rate of resupply by helicopter. Thus helicopters are no panacea to a logistician's ills, but they are vital in casualty evacuation and the urgent resupply of vital items. As the force moves away from the sea the helicopters will have to move with them. Fuel for the helicopters becomes a problem and some armies, like the British Army[1] have a ship-to-shore and onwards pipeline to solve this.

Those armies which maintain amphibious forces in peacetime also maintain a tailored logistic unit to support them. Because the logistic resupply task is a relatively small one these units are small too. The British marine logistic battalion has about 500 men in peace time, rising to just under a 1,000 when fully reinforced for war. The scale of the logistic resupply operation is small and, despite the range of specialisations, all the logistic elements can be commanded by one man. So the logistic battalion in support of an amphibios force is often in command of a truly composite unit with small sub-units of the four major logistic functions; supply, transport, repair and medical (see Figure 12.1.). These sub-units will be specifically tailored and trained to support an amphibiously-landed force of about 5,000 over a distance of 80km, with two major logistic areas, one at the beach-head and one just behind the combat logistic area (see Figure 12.2).

Airborne Operations

Operationally, the modern concept for airborne operations seems to have moved away from the massed divisional or corps drops of the Second World War and more towards the smaller end of the spectrum, where airborne forces are used for small *coup de main* operations of between battalion and brigade strength. Like amphibious operations, the existence or otherwise of air superiority drastically affects logistic support for airborne forces. For until other ground forces link up with the airborne force, resupply has to rely on air-landed or air-dropped stocks. Even given air superiority, resupply of airborne forces is more hazardous than that of amphibious forces. In the air resupply of amphibious forces, land and sea restricts enemy anti-aircraft weapons and leaves a relatively safe approach route over the sea. Airborne resupply has no such safe corridor and faces a three dimensional 360 degree threat.

Airborne forces are lightly equipped and have little integral equipment. Unless they can seize vehicles on landing to supplement the few that will be dropped with them, the awesome strategic mobility of airborne forces reduces to the mobility of the ordinary infantry foot soldier. Consequently, an airborne force tends to be very much a 'one shot' affair. It lands with what it has, and has to live off that small amount and what it can scavenge from the countryside and the enemy. Airborne logistic units are, therefore, even smaller than their amphibious comrades and, like them, are best brigaded into an airborne logistic battalion for a parachute brigade for example. Again like their amphibious comrades, they would expect to support a force of about 5,000 men over a distance no greater than 50–80 km and based on two logistic support areas: one at the landing site and one just behind the Combat Logistic Area (see Figure 12.3).

The logisticans within these units (see Figure 12.4.) have to be particularly

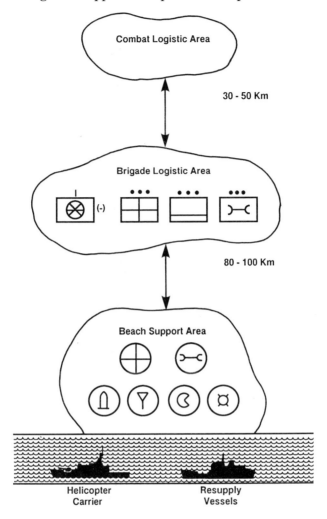

FIG. 12.2 Amphibious logistic operations

well trained and practised in their trades. They all have to be parachutists which is an arduous enough task in its own right. They also have to be trained in the ability to scavenge from the countryside and the enemy. Thus the transport unit will spend time training its drivers to drive any type of vehicle they might meet. Its supply company will maintain libraries of all known enemy ammunition and mine types in case they have to be used. It will have to keep the fast-fading military skill of butchery to reap the livestock harvest of the land. Every soldier in the unit, if not in the whole force, will carry siphons for captured stocks of fuel and its petroleum specialists will be expert at identifying captured fuel stocks. The repair unit will have trained its mechanics to meet strange engine types and to keep them going.

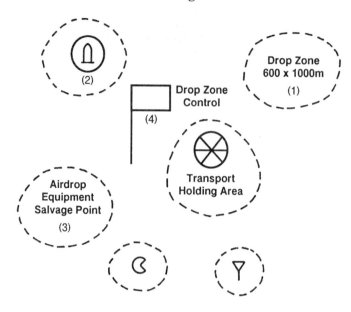

1. Drop Zone located so that aircraft do not need to overfly storage sites.

2. Ammunition kept as far away as possible from the other commodities.

3. A good guide would be 4 cargo parachutes recovered each hour.

4. The key factor is to clear the Drop Zone as quickly as possible and good control, sited close to the transport and mechanical handling equipment, is essential.

FIG. 12.3 Idealised airborne drop zone logistic layout

But the greatest challenge of airborne operations is that which is presented to the medical services. In airborne operations there can be little or no casualty evacuation. The only medical asset will be the airborne force's own 2nd Line medical unit. Because, routinely, such units are very much just treatment facilities to stabilise casualties sufficiently for evacuation, airborne medical units have to be reinforced with surgical teams and it is customary to find these teams as integral parts of an airborne formation's 2nd Line medical unit.

Airborne operations also call for two logistic skills that are rarely needed for more routine operations. These are the skills of 'rigging' (preparing) and 'dispatching' (dropping) parachute loads. Rigging relates to the preparation of loads so that, when dropped by parachute, they survive the descent in a useable condition. Most armies have conducted extensive trials to discover the safest type of platform on which to place their loads and almost all rely on

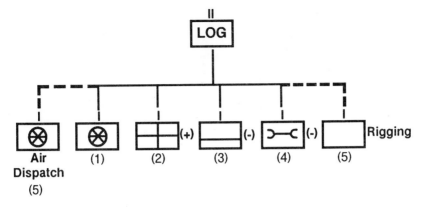

1.   Around 100 to 150 men but very few cargo vehicles. The vehicles will have little cargo capacity because, to be air-dropped, they must be small.

2.   Around 150 to 200 men because of reinforcement by surgical teams.

3.   Around 90 men only. Airborne brigades have a relatively small resupply requirement and supply personnel are needed only to control what stocks are held, to store what can be airdropped, and to scavange.

4.   Around 90 men only. An airborne brigade is not normally equipment intensive.

5.   Most armies have about 100 man specialist 'Rigging' and 'Air Dispatch' units, which prepare loads for airdropping. On operations, these units are based at the mounting airfield and thus the logistic battalion cannot exercise command of them when it is deployed on operations. They are, however, integral to the logistic resupply of an airborne formation.

FIG. 12.4 Airborne logistic battalion

some form of airbag which inflates prior to the platform landing and, in bursting, reduces the landing shock on the main platform. Despatchers are the men who load the aircraft and ensure that the loads exit safely. If either of these trades gets their task wrong, the load arrives with the paratroopers on the ground in an unuseable form.

Airmobile Operations

Following the path blazed by the French in Algeria and the US in Vietnam, most armies have studied the use of helicopter-transported forces, or airmobile forces as they have become known. The larger armies have introduced permanently configured airmobile formations. The US air cavalry division, the Russian *Desant* brigades, the 24th Airmobile Brigade in the UK and the *Luftlande* Brigade in Germany are examples. The operational roles of such forces are in some areas very similar to those of airbone forces: *coup de main*

operations of up to brigade strength over distances restricted only by helicopter range. However the more likely use is as a counter-penetration force. In
this role, the airmobile brigade is flown ahead of an enemy formation that has
broken through, digs in and then uses its infantry anti-tank missiles and its
armed helicopters to halt the penetration. Time is gained for a conventional
armoured formation, which moves at a speed of 40kph whereas the airmobile
forces helicopters will move at around 250kph, to arrive and complete the
destruction of the enemy by an attack. Thus an airmobile force in the counter-
penetration role will normally be operating within reasonable reach of other
ground troops and this has some effect on its logistic support. If friendly forces
are nearby the airmobile force follows the concept of 'plugging into' the logistic
support of that friendly force. Under this concept the airmobile force links in to
the resupply system of the troops in whose area it is fighting. This enables its
own integral support to be kept to the bare minimum and releases valuable
helicopters for more pressing operational tasks.

But plugging-in brings with it its own problems, especially in NATO where
there is little commonality in equipment. Thus an airmobile Netherlands
formation might be plugged-in to a French ground force. In the past there
would have been little that the French force could have done to help. NATO
standardisation has helped here and, if the French force's resources allowed
(and as will be discussed later, this is a big 'if') much could be done. Fuel could
be supplied to the helicopters (the fuel tankers might not be the same but
NATO standardisation has ensured that all the couplings are compatible).
Small arms ammunition, some missiles such as Milan, and most artillery
ammunition could be supplied to the whole airmobile force. Similarly, the
medical facilities of the ground force could be made available and would
require only reinforcement by the medical teams of the airmobile formation's
own 2nd Line medical unit.

The 'if' of this particular situation revolves around the fact that much
depends on whether the French ground force has the stocks to give. Counter-
penetration forces are used because the enemy seems likely to break, or has
broken, through. There is, therefore, the risk that the ground force would
need everything it has, to support its own forces. Who would be fighting
desperately to stem the enemy onslaught. There is also the 'friction' factor of
war to consider. In a period of intensive activity for the ground force, when its
headquarters and units would be moving, it would be difficult for the airmobile force (in a foreign language) to find the responsible headquarters, and
the responsible officers within that headquarters, in order to co-ordinate the
plug-in. To balance this rather pessimistic summary of the co-operation
difficulties involved, it should be said that the likely area of the airmobile
operation (in the region of 3rd Line logistic units) does make resupply from
the ground force's stocks more likely and the airmobile force should have
enough immediate stocks with it to ensure that there is time for the vital
liaison to take place.

Fortunately, an airmobile force (like its amphibious and airborne counterparts) has a relatively small requirement for logistic support. Its infantry,

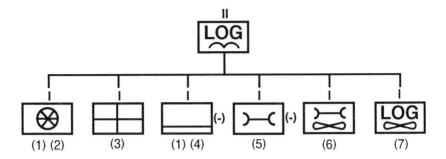

1.   An airmobile brigade's logistic requirements are relatively small. Transport and supply priority is given to aviation fuel supply.

2.   Airmobile artillery tends to be of a smaller calibre than normal field artillery. This keeps the guns light and therefore more airmobile. However, this means that an airmobile artillery unit cannot use the stocks of an in-place line artillery unit and thus its support has to be larger than it might be.

3.   Unlike an airborne medical unit, an airmobile medical unit can use the medical facilities of the in-place formations.

4.   60 - 80 men only.

5.   80 - 100 men only.

6.   The aviation maintenance unit is the key to the logistic support of an airmobile formation.

7.   If support helicopters are commanded by the air force, they normally bring with them a specialist helicopter support unit.

FIG. 12.5 Airmobile logistic battalion

despite the introduction of various types of very small all-terrain vehicles to help mobility, is very much foot-bound once landed. It might have integral artillery but is more likely to rely on its own mortars supplemented by whatever artillery is in the operational area. If it has integral artillery then the logistic resupply problem becomes greater. Helicopters would have to be diverted from other fly-in tasks to move resupply ammunition to the guns, unless stocks exist nearby of the same calibre. But most airmobile artillery is of a smaller calibre than that in use with ordinary artillery units and often the only source of resupply is from the airmobile formation's own operational base.

Consequently, an airmobile formation's 2nd Line support (see Figure 12.5.) need not be large as an airmobile formation has so little heavy equipment other than the helicopters themselves, and a brigade could be supported by a composite logistic battalion with companies from the four main logistic groupings. These companies will have two elements. A very small 'fly-in'

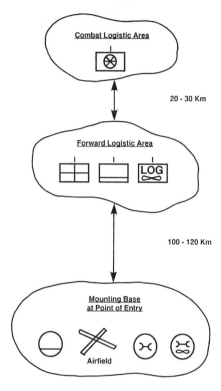

FIG. 12.6 Airmobile logistic layout

element and a much larger 'road tail'. Once deployed, the logistic battalion will form two groupings: a base and a forward element right behind the combat logistic area. The fly-in element is there to supplement the supplies delivered in the first 48 hours or so with the combat troops, which adds up to a surprisingly small amount of stocks, and to conduct the reconnaissance and liaison with the host formation. The road tail will carry a further three to five days worth of stocks for the force with priority being given to those items particular to airmobile operations. The whole force would rely on plugging-in for everything else it could not bring with it.

The key to airmobile operations are the transport helicopters that fly such a force in, and the armed helicopters that provide so much of an airmobile formation's 'teeth'. Logistically, helicopters both provide solutions and cause problems. Because of the helicopter's speed and range (see Figure 12.7.), it can return to refuel and rearm with little adverse affect on the battle. By doing so it removes the need for one of the ground resupply loops and releases those resources for other tasks.

Conversely, helicopters are fragile complicated beasts which gulp fuel. This fragility helps helicopter anti-tank missile resupply. Wargaming and modelling would seem to show that helicopters are likely to be lost faster than their stocks of missiles become exhausted. What may be a comfort to the logistician

Helicopter Type	Maximum Speed (Km/h)	Typical Range (Km/h)	Load (Kg)
Aerospatiale/Westland GAZELLE	264	360	700
Aerospatial/Westland PUMA	257	580	1,500
Westland LYNX	322	540	1,360
Sikorsky UH60 BLACKHAWK	296	600	3,630
Bell HUEY	204	400	2,000
Boeing CH47	304	185	12,700
Mil Mi - 26 HALO	295	800	20,000

FIG. 12.7 Helicopter speeds, ranges and loads

might not be so comforting to the helicopter crews! But a helicopter requires a considerable and highly trained technical ground crew to keep it flying. There are so many things that can go wrong with such a machine. Helicopters have to spend hours on the ground being serviced (how long depends on the aircraft type) for every hour spent in the air. Intensive helicopter usage on one day could drastically reduce the numbers of helicopters available to fly on the next. Hard-working aircraft mechanics can do some maintenance at night and careful tasking of aircraft can also reduce the operational penalties. On balance, the helicopter's ability to come back to resupply at what have become known as Forward Arming and Refuelling Points (FARPs!) largely negates these problems.

Counter Revolutionary War Operations

A tendency has grown up in Western European armies to regard operations outside the NATO area as relatively simple logistic exercises. In the period from 1945 to the 1970s perhaps strategically this was true. Most of the colonial compaigns fought in this period were against relatively light opposition waging some sort of revolutionary war. There were periods of high intensity operations but, generally, mechanised forces were rarely engaged, and it is these that generate the greatest demand for logistic resources. Another factor involved was that, as a result of hangovers from colonial expansion or the Second World War, in or near to the theatre of conflict was either a sizeable logistic base or something that could be built up into one. Thus if a campaign's intensity increased, there was normally a stockpile of ex-Second World War equipment, good enough in quality to match the weapons of most of the likely lighter armed opposition, in a strategic depot or other source close by. British operations in Malaya and Borneo could rely on the huge logistic base in Singapore. In Korea the US could use the huge base they had built up in Japan at the end of the Second World War. The French were less well off for strategic depots in Vietnam. For their campaign in Algeria they had metropolitan France just across the Mediterranean and a sizeable military infrastructure in Algeria and elsewhere in North Africa. However, as time passed, the scale and nature of the opposition to Western armies grew. The French in Indo-China were the first to experience this. Their Viet-Minh enemy put formed divisions into the field supported by all arms. Similarly, the export of Soviet small arms and light weapons meant that in some areas the insurgents had better weaponry than the government forces. Consequently, logistic support for counter-revolutionary warfare very much depends on the stage of revolutionary warfare that the insurgency has reached.

Most military writers divide insurgency into three phases. The first phase is when the insurgents start their campaign and have little support. It is waged in selected areas of the countryside and in the cities. In the countryside the aim of the insurgents is to win the hearts and minds of the local population by small-scale actions against police and military and the assassination of unpopular officials and landlords. In the cities, the insurgents' aim is to use small two-or three-man cells of urban terrorists to provoke the government into repressive measures that will create a source of recruits and funding for the insurgents' cause. In the second phase of an insurgency, company and battalion level actions help the insurgents to win control of specific regions. Their aim is to create areas where they rule in order that they can build themselves up without interference from government forces. In the third phase, the insurgents engage government forces with brigade and divisional formations of all arms and attempt to overthrow the established power by force of arms. Real life insurgencies are often not so neat as this. At any one time the insurgency can be at Phase One in one particular area, at Phase Two in another and at Phase Three somewhere else. Thus the South Vietnamese and their allies faced a Phase One insurgency in some of the areas around Saigon while in others they faced actions at Phase Two level and along their borders with Cambodia and Laos faced a situation that had reached Phase Three. With the deployment of regular North Vietnamese forces, it must have seemed to the South Vietnamese more like a conventional invasion than a counter-revolutionary war struggle.

Logistic support for counter-insurgency forces during Phase One of an insurgency is very simple. There are just not the size and scale of operations to require the resupply of ammunition at intensive rates. Those problems that do arise stem from the fragmentation of the counter-insurgency forces into a myriad of small patrol bases as the government forces take the battle into the areas where the insurgents are trying to establish themselves. These require 2nd Line logistic units to be partially broken-up amongst them. Constructing and stocking (normally with 14 days supply of all commodities) these bases takes some logistic effort but is a relatively simple task. Before the arrival of the helicopter these bases were resupplied by weekly road convoys and the resupply vehicles often provided inviting targets for the insurgents. The helicopter changed this significantly and for a halcyon period made logistic resupply, and the all-important casualty evacuation, during Phase One extremely easy. Unfortunately, the arrival of effective man-portable anti-aircraft missiles now makes helicopter resupply more hazardous and requires escort helicopters and countermeasures to defeat the electronic heads on the missiles. Even given the increased danger to helicopters, they are still a safer and surer measure of resupply than road convoys would be.

But providing support to military forces is not the only task for logisticians during Phase One of a counter-insurgency. This phase is very much one of fighting for the hearts and minds of the local population and logistic units can play their part. The medical service has an obvious role to play in supplementing the existing medical facilities. Engineer teams can do much to improve the local infrastructure by construction of roads and buildings and digging wells and providing electric power. The supply service could inject much-needed funds into the local markets. But care has to be taken here; especially if Western troops are involved in a Third World country. The relatively sophisticated tastes and high purchasing power of Western troops can increase prices for goods out of the range of the local population. This can make the Western troops unpopular, even hated, by the very people they are there to try to help. Local purchase can play its part in stimulating the local economy but its application needs to be carefully planned. It is not a panacea. Unfortunately, those responsible for allocating shipping space often regard it as such. If the magic wand of 'Local Purchase' or 'Local Resources' is waved, logistic units can be saved from the order of battle of the deploying force. This is invariably a short-sighted and short-lived economy measure.

> We have a claim on the output of the arsenals of London as well as of Hanyang, and what is more, it is to be delivered to us by the enemy's own transport corps. This is the sober truth, not a joke?[2]

If logistic units' tasks during Phase One are to help their own forces and the local population, it is not to help the insurgents. During Phase One of revolutionary war the task of the insurgents is to build up their strength. In historical campaigns there have been a number of examples where the insurgents obtained medical supplies, arms and ammunition from the government forces, either by taking them by force or by bribery. Corrupt British soldiers within the Tel Aviv ordnance depot supplied a number of items to the Jewish insurgent forces, one of which was rumoured to be a Centurion tank! The depot's highly-decorated commanding officer was not involved but still found himself court-martialled and one of the last prisoners in the Tower of London. Combat units during Phase One of an insurgency are needed to take the war to the enemy and there will be few available for escorts or static guards. This means logistic units need to be able to defend themselves, especially their road convoys, against attack, and must have sufficient integrity and audit checks not to succumb to bribery.

The greater intensity of Phase Two of an insurgency increases the load for the logistician as well as for the combat soldier. Phase One logistic operations still have to be supported but there now has to be special provision for the peaks of activity that will take place as large enemy units either spring their ambushes and assaults or are trapped by government forces. Rather like a combat reserve, these peaks require a logistic reserve of evacuation and resupply helicopters and some means, road or air, of getting ammunition resupply through to the artillery (who only now will start to play a significant role in the campaign). The maintenance service's main point of effort will be the support of the helicopter fleet and the repair of the night vision devices that might give the government forces the technological edge in close combat with the insurgents. During Phase Two, logistic ammunition and weapon dumps become even more vulnerable because the size of an attacking insurgent force could well be greater than the logistic defenders. As a result, the number of these dumps has to be reduced and, if combat troops are not available to provide security, the dumps have to be moved to safer areas (which normally means away from the troops they support) or the logistic units need increased weapon scales so that they can defend both themselves and their dumps.

The insurgents' Phase Three, when full-sized formations emerge to engage government forces in open combat, results in the logistician facing the challenges of high-intensity war while the problems of the earlier phases remain. On the positive side there is the fact that the insurgents are unlikely to have air superiority. This is a major plus. It means that resupply can be carried out during daylight, which makes it faster and probably safer. On the debit side, there will still be no real safe rear areas and combat soldiers will be fighting the insurgents and not available for security duties. This means logistic units will have to spend more effort in defending themselves, which in turn means they will have less time to carry out their logistic function.

Lest all these challenges might seem almost overwhelming, it pays the counter-insurgent logistician to consider the problems and difficulties of his revolutionary opposite number. The first and foremost of these is actually being able to assemble the supplies for waging war. If there is a convenient and friendly border, and most successful insurgencies have had such, the means for waging war can be assembled there; as can the base hospitals, training camps and repair shops. But the supplies are needed inside the area of operations and the insurgent logistician has the problem of getting them there. Movement will have to be by night and vehicles probably cannot be used. Everything must be man or animal-packed. The insurgent resupply routes are even more liable to ambush and interdiction than those of the government forces, for the latter are likely to have air superiority. Once in the operational area the stocks have got to be stored safely. This is difficult when the government forces have the location of these supply dumps at the top of their target priority list. It is no wonder that insurgent offensives take time to prepare and mount and have the stop-go rhythm of jungle operations. Once action is joined, human porterage cannot resupply at the intensive rates needed by combat troops fighting hard. Thus, in Vietnam, General Giap and his successors often had to withdraw from an action against the French, South Vietnamese or Americans because, having failed to succeed initially, supplies could not be delivered in enough quantities and fast enough to enable the action to be carried on against growing opposition. As if supplying their side were not difficult enough for the insurgents, there is the problem of casualty evacuation and treatment. Casualties cannot be left to the enemy because, above all, an insurgency is an intelligence war and too much information can be obtained from wounded picked up by government forces. Neither are there any helicopters for speedy evacuation. Probably the nearest safe hospital will be some days' march away from the combat area. It should come as no surprise that insurgent forces can rarely meet the Six Hour Rule for casualty evacuation and that, consequently, insurgent casualty rates, in terms of number of dead to number of wounded, are much worse than those of government forces. Put simply, if an insurgent receives anything other than a light wound he is likely to die; whereas all but the most severely wounded government soldiers are likely to survive.

All in all, perhaps it is better to be a government logistician than it is to be a logistician on the insurgent side.

13.

Logistic Support for Special Climates and Terrain

Jungle Operations

To the Western eye, reared on film and television images of jungle being a thick and impenetrable hell, it must seem certain that tactical and logistic operations are slowed down in jungle operations. There is also the impression that impenetrable jungle covers all hot equatorial lands. This is far from true. Most of the land has been cleared of its native vegetation and in equatorial countries there are the types of terrain that would be found anywhere else: cleared cultivated plains and intensively farmed lowlands. But where in the West one would find river meadows, one finds jungle swamp; where one would find upland forest, one finds primary jungle. Nor, to the soldier who has to struggle through it, is all jungle the same. In primary jungle the trees grow to enormous heights and, although their crowns present a thick screen from above, undergrowth is almost non-existent and there is a considerable distance between the trunks of individual trees. Secondary jungle is where the hand of man or some natural disaster has cleared the primary jungle. The jungle, in regenerating itself, springs into life with thickets and clumps of competing vegetation that make it almost impassable. Like primary jungle, secondary jungle also presents an almost impenetrable canopy to view from above. It is secondary jungle that is the setting used for so many films.

All terrain has some influence on logistics, if only that some are easier for logistic operations than others. Jungle would seem to be a prime candidate for a type of terrain that would slow down tactical operations to a tempo that would be easy for the logistician to support; even given the problems that that sort of terrain would obviously cause for the logistician as well as the tactician. But man has an ability to fight intensively in almost any sort of climate and over any sort of ground, and jungle is no exception. The Second World War in the Pacific and in Burma, showed that war could be waged in jungle as intensively as it could be waged on the open plains of Europe and the French and US experience in Vietnam reinforces this.

But supporting a jungle war does create special challenges to the logistician. The first of these is normally the limited infrastructure in the theatre of operations. Jungle terrain is sparsely populated and the roads, rarely surfaced, will be limited and vulnerable to closure by mining and the weather. Railways would more than likely be non-existent. There might be light aircraft landing grounds and temporary airstrips, but these will rarely be all-weather and unlikely to be able to take large military aircraft. Thus jungle terrain in the past imposed a tempo on tactical operations which was linked to the ability of logistic units to bring forward enough supplies to enable intensive war to be waged. This imposed an almost 'stop-go' tempo to jungle wars. When logistic risks were taken to break out of this cycle and they did not come off, the result could be catastophic, as for example with the Mutaguchi's 15th Japanese Army in 1944 Burma.

Mutaguchi had planned that his troops would be able to seize the stocks built up at Imphal by General Slim's British 14th Army. Consequently, the Japanese had moved carrying only the bare minimum of supplies. Imphal and its stocks were not surrendered by the British, but held. Mutaguchi had not foreseen this possibility. The monsoons prevented any large-scale Japanese resupply and the 15th Army had to retreat. By the end of the retreat, the Japanese had lost 65,000 dead, less than half of whom were battle casualties. The majority had been lost to malaria and starvation.

To be certain of success, supply dumps need to be built up before offensives can start and, once the battle has been won, traditionally the pursuit has normally faltered in front of the next serious opposition. The campaign would be then be stalled until more ammunition could be brought up to continue the offensive. But risks can be taken successfully in jungle operations. The British General Slim, having fought his tactical battle around the towns of Imphal and Kohima, decided to use the stockpiles at Imphal to power his pursuit of the beaten Japanese. Slim gambled that few logistic resources would be needed against his beaten foe and that, when the pursuit reached the point that it outstripped the land supply chain, airdropped resupply would be sufficient to keep up the momentum of the advance and thus overcome the 'stop-go' effect of jungle operations.

> The vulnerable artery is the line of communications winding through the jungle. Have no line of communication on the jungle floor. Bring in the goods like Father Christmas down the chimney.[1]

For modern day jungle operations the airdropped avenue for resupply is still open, but it has largely been replaced by the ubiquitous and logistically invaluable helicopter. It is an awkward decision for commanders whether those helicopters are used for logistic resupply or combat troop transport. The US 1st Air Cavalry Division in Vietnam was sufficiently lavishly equipped with helicopters to be able to do both. Few armies are so well off.

If the transporter is faced with a shortage of roads and a reliance on the fast, but logistically lightweight, fall-back of air-drop and helicopter resupply, the supplier's problems are the relatively simple ones of building up enough stocks along restricted resupply routes quickly enough to support the commander's plan. The maintainer's problems are relatively simple too.

Repair priority must go to the helicopters and, while a jungle war might at times be as mechanically intensive as any in Europe, it is more likely to be a largely dismounted infantry affair with less equipments to maintain. Tropical conditions do, however, play havoc with complicated electrical equipment and significant repair effort has to be allocated to keep the myriad of electronic devices required by a modern army fit for action.

Of all the logistic functions it is the medical service for which the jungle presents the greatest challenge. It is not just European armies who face this jungle challenge. Indigenous armies face very similar problems. The tropical jungle environment breeds disease. A significant part of the available medical effort has to be devoted to prevention rather than to cure. General Slim's Second World War Burma Army found itself decimated by disease. The widespead use of penicillin and strict hygiene measures, for which commanders were made personally responsible, helped to reduce his daily sick lists. However, the jungle environment still took its toll and produced rates for sickness double and treble that of the European theatre. Since the Second World War, medical science has discovered antibiotics as its modern day equivalent of penicillin. But the need to make tactical commanders directly responsible for preventive hygiene measures remains. The jungle is unforgiving in this respect.

The jungle also has its effect on the recovery rate of patients. In an equatorial climate, patients are more vulnerable to secondary infections and the normal healing rates for wounds are exceeded. Field and General Hospitals need to be sited in areas where the climatic effects are reduced. Hill stations and seaside locations historically seem to have been the most beneficial sites.

All these specific functional challenges pale almost into insignificance compared with the overall logistic challenge of getting resupply and casualty evacuation to 1st and 2nd Line. If the jungle is a severly constraining factor to the logistic functions at 3rd and 4th Line, at 1st and 2nd Line its effect is felt most of all. In essence, it is a problem of distribution, hampered and clogged at every step by the vegetation and poor tracks. The task is to get the supplies to the front line troops but, as is so often the case, it is the most difficult problem of all. In dense jungle, with no roads or tracks, the most modern mechanical handling devices are of little use. All but the smallest all-terrain vehicles find themselves bogged down. Those vehicles that can be used will consume almost twice the normal amount of fuel as they stay in almost permanent all-wheel drive and keep to the lowest gears. The artillery, more often further back than the close combat troops, are difficult to resupply with the amount of ammunition they would wish to fire. However, if artillery firing positions are selected not from the best tactical viewpoint, but from a best possible logistic resupply perspective, the guns can normally be supplied. For the combat infantryman, resupply relies largely on porters, supplemented by mules, light all-terrain vehicles and helicopters when these are available.

The most difficult supplies to get forward to the combat troops are liquids. For both water and fuel, most modern armies now rely on bulk tankers, the mobility of which in jungle is almost nil. Although the fuel requirement for jungle operations overall might be lower than for a mechanised formation in Europe, those vehicles that are being used will consume fuel at a voracious rate. Bulk liquid resupply has to be abandoned in favour of jerrycans and this imposes a load on the 2nd Line logistic units who have to transfer liquids from tankers to cans. Water, too, is consumed at a great rate by troops involved in jungle operations. A planning figure of 20 litres per man per day would be a conservative estimate and this does not include water for other uses like communal cooking and bathing. The soldiers of most armies only carry about 2–4 litres as part of their personal equipment. This means that there needs to be a constantly moving water resupply chain straight to the front line, and one which needs to move in daylight rather than the darkness of the more traditional resupply chain. Much of this liquid movement, especially to the front line troops, has to be by man-pack. Man-packing liquids is terribly fatiguing for the porter. The constantly shifting load wears down the carrier faster than an equivalent solid load. It is for this task that platoon sergeants reserve their fittest men; or those that have annoyed them!

Desert Operations

Desert operations are almost the antithesis of jungle operations. While there are areas of poor traffic (or 'going' as the British call it) in desert regions, almost all of the terrain can be used for tracked movement and most by all-wheel drive vehicles. Frontages of units are vast, dispersion is the norm. Instead of the restricted fields of view and fire of the jungle, the desert in most conditions presents almost perfect visibility and target acquisition conditions. Long-range engagements become the norm and the desert seems ideal for mobile armoured warfare. Instead of the jungle's humidity there is the glaring heat of the sun and the freezing cold of the desert night. Consequently, the wise logistician reaches for his history books to profit from the lessons of past campaigns.

The liberation of Kuwait in 1991 highlighted many of the lessons learned by armies which had previously operated in the desert. The historical retrieval cells of the armies involved, less the French element which were well practised in desert operations, were inundated with queries from commanders keen to prepare themselves, their formations and units better for the desert battles ahead. Understandably, the tactical lessons were more easily found than those for logistics. Conversely, the tactical lessons depended very much on equipment and weapon types which had changed. But the logistic lessons had changed little.

On the supply front, history and current experience shows that, overall for a formation, long-range ammunition rates almost double while close quarter ammunition rates reduce by a third. Thus divisional loading tables have to be rejigged to reflect the greater use of artillery and the lesser use of mortar and small arms ammunition. In modern armies the anti-tank guided missile becomes the ammunition that is like gold-dust to the front line units. But the complicated insides of modern missiles can be degraded by high temperatures or the direct rays of the sun. The suppliers have to remember to keep them in their transit containers and in the shade for as long as possible. Even simple propellant charges can have their useful life reduced by temperatures over 35 degrees Celsius. At around 45 degrees Celsius (111 degrees Fahrenheit), the white phosphorus of most smoke shells will liquefy and start to leak from its containers. Because of the lack of cover, all supply stocks have to be dispersed over a far greater area. A materiel company's European area of one square kilometre becomes three times that. The distances for other supply items increase by at least this rate. This dispersion slows up supply responsiveness as its soldiers trudge across strength-sapping sand in oppressive heat.

Wheeled vehicle fuel consumption rates from the Second World War Western Desert campaign were remarkably similar to those in the 1991 liberation of Kuwait; tracked vehicle consumption rates were not, largely because of the huge technical difference between the simple engines of the 1940 tanks and the gas turbines or advanced diesels of modern armoured fighting vehicles. There was a similarity between both campaigns. Fuel supply and distribution became a major factor in war planning and tanks and other fighting vehicles increased their rates of consumption some one-and-a-half times above their European theatre norms.

You do not become an expert in the use of the sun compass overnight.[2]

The greatest challenge to the transportation function is to be able to link up with the troops it is to support. Navigation in the desert is not easy. The dispersion of the desert battlefield puts units further apart, makes them more difficult to find and requires the resupply vehicles to travel further. Unless air superiority is held, the lack of natural cover makes movement in daylight perilous. Modern technology can make it easier for navigation. The use of hand held or vehicle mounted navigation aids, often linked directly to a satellite, made finding the way across the Kuwaiti Desert in 1991 simpler for those that had them.

Unfortunately the short desert night leaves precious little time for the resupply to link up with the combat troops; nor is it any protection against a high technology enemy air force. The Iraqi Army found this out to their cost in 1991. Once the air campaign started, almost all resupply to the Iraqi dug-in formations was stopped. The advancing Coalition ground forces overran Iraqi units which had not been resupplied since the start of the air campaign and had been forced to live off what they had; and what they had reflected their Soviet mentors' preoccupation with ammunition. Beaten Iraqi units' ammunition levels were rarely low but in almost every case the unit had been on half rations or worse. The traditional way to carry out logistic resupply in an adverse air situation is to split the resupply convoys into small separate detachments, each of which strikes off on its own route across the desert. Historically, many of these got through. Unfortunately for the Iraqis, such was the Coalition air superiority and technological edge, that even this method did not work. Their small detachments met the fate of their larger brethren.

The desert reserves its harshest treatment for equipment. All moving parts are subject to the abrasive effect of sand and rocks. To keep vehicles moving takes a very high level of maintenance indeed. Sand temperatures of as much as 74 degrees Celsius (165 degrees Fahrenheit) doubles tyre usage. As much as 40 per cent of the tyres of a unit can be flat after a long cross-country move. Every vehicle has to carry extra fan belts. Every moving part has to be checked; steering, transmission shafts, bolts and spocket nuts can all suffer along with the more obvious track links, pads and torsion bars. The consumption of spare parts will be almost double European levels. Everything that can expand in the searing heat of the desert day, or contract in the cold of the desert night, will do so. Power steering, hydraulics and air pressure cylinders will leak. Oil seals will blow and almost every vehicle temperature gauge will read up to 10 degrees Celcius (20 degrees Fahrenheit) hotter than normal. Complicated electronic equipment can find itself operating at temperatures far above its design limits with circuits short-circuited by fine desert sand that gets in everywhere. Special desert maintenance-free batteries can be bought. If these are not available, ordinary wet batteries need their specific gravity increased to between 1.200 and 1.225 sg or have to be filled with sulphuric acid electrolyte, if they are to perform well during the heat of daylight hours. Unfortunately, this reduces their efficiency during the cold nights. Even precision optics can be discoloured, and thereby degraded under the glare of the direct midday sun and have to be kept under cover.

In the desert, the real key to the maintenance battle is which side possesses the battlefield at the end of the day. Broken-down and battle-damaged vehicles, and there are many of these on a desert battlefield, can be repaired; but only if the repair teams can get to them or recover them back to the workshops. If the battlefield is lost, then so are all the vehicle casualties on it. In the Second World War desert battles, this fact was appreciated by both sides. Tactical engagements sprang up as both sides' repair team protection parties clashed in no-mans-land.

The desert is only slightly less harsh on man. Unacclimatised Westerners dehydrate rapidly. Even acclimatised troops need prodigious amounts of water if they are to engage in any strenuous activity in the sun. Water is available in the desert, either from isolated open wells in wadis or from deep boreholes. Often highly saline, it can calcify in cooling systems and corrode metal, as well as a Westerner's insides. A requirement for about 40 litres of water per day per man is a good planning figure and seems to have changed little over history. 'Sweet' (potable) drinking water is important as it helps reduce the amount of hygiene-related disease, and for its effect on morale. Most armies possess reverse osmosis water purification units to turn saline water into something more useable. The water they produce can be too salty to the taste and often drinkable water in plastic containers has to be brought in from outside the theatre of operations. Even the availability of water is no guarantee that soldiers will drink it. If stored in the sun, water can reach blood temperature, at which it is distasteful to drink. Sometimes some sort of cooling, either natural or artificial, is needed before soldiers will swallow it.

During the liberation of Kuwait, a number of US Army water tankers were equipped with small lightweight refrigeration units to bring the water down to a temperature where soldiers would drink it.

Just as the desert sand abrades metal, it also abrades man. Sunburn can lay low Western units. Wind and dust attacks the eyes, nose and any exposed flesh. Consumption rates of lip salves and skin creams quadruple. Refrigeration is vital to keep these, and other medical supplies, within their designed temperature limits. One of a field commander's priorities for the use of field generators must be his formation's medical units. Minor sickness in the desert can have major complications. The heat increases the chance of sanitary infection and proper field hygiene is vital to reduce daily sick lists. The issue of plastic throw-away plates and eating utensils was a water-saving measure by the Coalition forces in 1991. But it seems to have helped reduce the British force's incidence of hygiene-related diseases some 50 per cent below historical rates. Commanders and soldiers at all levels were aware of this:

> Even washing hands before meals and after toilet functions became compulsive, and not just compulsory.[3]

Yet, for all the medical dangers, provided a unit follows its preventive hygiene rules rigorously, the desert can be a surprisingly healthy place. Once troops become acclimatised and used to living and operating in its conditions, daily sick lists reduce to normal and even below the norm.

Snow Operations

The heading of 'Snow Operations' for this section, rather than the more often used 'Arctic Warfare', is deliberate. Snow is not just limited to the far northern and far southern climes. It affects operations in the high country of most temperate nations and, in the winter months, lies like a blanket across continental temperate lands. Thus, in Europe for example, armies need to be prepared for, at worst, some three months of operations in snow. They rarely are. Exercising unequipped and unprepared troops in the snow increases sick lists and accidents. The short winter days restrict the amount of time that can be spent exercising and winter exercises are less cost effective than those in the spring and autumn. Fighting in the snow imposes its own disciplines and speed. Most 'temperate climes' armies would rather leave such considerations to specialised mountain warfare or northern climes troops.

Ski instructors with their numerous coloured waxes identify many types of snow. For the logistician there are just two: dry snow and wet snow. Dry snow is found in the centre of the great continental masses (Russia and Canada for example). Wet snow is found near coasts or in mountains where the composition of the snow is affected by the presence of moisture from clouds or the sea. Each presents challenges to those who would wish to live, fight and resupply in the snow. But, of the two, soldiers much prefer to operate in dry snow. It is easier to keep warm. Wet snow soaks clothing and breaks down insulation layers and increases cold casualties. Wet snow freezes and thaws more often than dry; so accidents happen more often. Wet cold happens more often than not in high country, which means that level terrain is at a premium and resupply routes are tortuous, difficult and limited to valleys. Hence the preference of soldiers for the dry cold of the great plains and its less strict impositions on warfare.

Perhaps snow's greatest effect is its reduction of speed of movement. Modern armies are all based around the need for mobile warfare. Snow hampers all movement; whether the movement is that of the advancing infantryman trying to run in the assault through snow one metre deep (rather like running through thigh-high waves at the beach) or the loaded resupply vehicle trying to push through a snow blocked or drifted road. Movement timings have to be increased by 25 per cent in good weather and more than 50 per cent in bad. Wheeled vehicles, even with snow tyres or snow chains fall behind their tracked comrades. Before the invention of sophisticated night vision aids this was all partly counterbalanced by the length of the winter night. This gave the logistician more time to get the resupply to the troops. But modern surveillance aids take away some of the protective cloak of this darkness. In good weather, thermal imaging can highlight labouring logistic resupply vehicles against their cold background. Navigation is as hard as in the desert. On the great plains, and even in the mountains, snow cloaks landmarks and makes getting lost much easier.

Snow can cloak static logistic sites and make camouflage of ammunition stacks and other piles of supplies easier. But it clogs the routes to and around these sites. Traditional logistic unit siting distances have to be adjusted. In mountainous country the heights of the hill and mountain tops makes all but very high trajectory weapon systems useless. Consequently, logistic sites can be picked closer to the front than hitherto. Much depends on the range of the enemy's mortars but, if shielded by high ground, the stockpiles could probably move as close to the front as two kilometres. On flat tundra this option is not open but, as snow has a dampening effect on ordinary high explosive shells, risks can be taken with putting ammunition stacks closer together. The same is not true of petroleum sites. Paradoxically, the greatest fear in the snow is of fire. Petroleum stacks have no in-built protection and it is unwise to ignore safety distances in their case. In both flat and mountainous terrain, however, considerable engineer effort has to be given to keeping the logistic routes open.

In mountainous areas the flat ground on which to site logistic units is hard to find. More often than not, the flat areas are along the valley bottoms which are also the main operational and resupply routes. As a result, the logistic units are vulnerable to enemy action against the roads. The result is that logistic units spread along the bottom of the valley in small, uneconomic penny-packets. While this reduces the danger from enemy action, it means that all basic logistic activities take much longer than they should (by as much as half again) and further restricts the flow of supplies. Where there are mountain lakes or fjord-like country, the ice sheets can be used as logistic dumps. The Red Army built a winter-only railway across Lake Lagoda in order to get supplies through to the besieged city of Leningrad during the Second World War. Alongside the railway they also built a vehicle highway. Corduroy roads (roads built of logs) are the normal method of surfacing such routes and logistic resupply sites can even be laid on the ice.

The ice can be especially useful for temporary petroleum bulk fuel farms. The fabric, rubberised 'pillow' tanks that hold the fuel need a flat surface if they are not to 'wander' under the subtle pull of gravity. If an ice-sheet is to be used, an insulating layer such as logs needs to be laid between the pillow tanks and the ice[4].

The transporter's task of distributing supplies is made harder by the constricted and vulnerable routes along the valley in mountainous country, and in flat tundra by the difficulty of finding their destinations. Both are subject to the clogging effect of snow and of bad weather. Off- and On-Loading times are much increased because mechanical handling equipment bogs in as soon as it picks up its load. The extra weight of the load suddenly makes the handling equipment heavier than it was. The packed snow, over which it moved quite easily to reach the cargo truck, suddenly gives way and the wheels of the handling equipment disappear. If the packed snow does not give way, it turns into sheet ice. Chains are needed for the fork lifts' wheels and the tyres suffer from this and the reduced elasticity caused by the cold. Special operating aprons have to be made of a location is to be used for any length of time. Every snowfall has to be cleared off these aprons, not a popular task for the soldiers working on the site.

For the supplier, snow operations bring their own changes to working practices. High-angle mortar and artillery rounds become the prime ammunition task with special fuses to ensure that the shells explode on top of, rather than in, the snow. Packaging for guided missile rounds becomes even more important to ensure that no snow gets inside to melt, and then freeze, and thereby gum up expensive electronic warheads.

Working and fighting in the snow requires a high calorific intake and most armies have special high calorie 'Arctic' ration packs for their soldiers. This, plus the snow's action as a natural refrigerator, somewhat eases the supply of rations. The provision of water for all purposes is not so simple; it freezes. Many a unit has been caught unawares by water tankers freezing and splitting, and then losing their contents as the temperature rises and the water melts and escapes through a crack. If small heaters are not to be fitted to water trailers, containers have to be loaded to 10 per cent less than their maximum contents to allow for freezing which creates an appreciable additional logistic load. More trailers have to be shifted for the same volume of water. Even the obvious remedy of melting snow to obtain water is not that easy. For a given volume, it takes more than four times the equivalent amount of snow and this requires heat and time, both in short supply for front-line troops.

In snow operations the fuel load is considerable. Every vehicle consumes at least one third more than its temperate 'norm' both because of the road conditions and because engines are kept running continuously to prevent both the engine and vehicle crews from freezing. Once stopped in snow conditions engines, despite the use of light specialised winter grade oils and greases (another item that the supplier has to remember to bring with him), are difficult to restart and most armies have some sort of cold-start cartridge to kick-start recalcitrant engines into life. Care has to be taken that the correct grade fuels are used. Diesel can gel in extreme cold and, if an 'arctic' diesel is not being used, kerosene has to be mixed with it. The provision of fuel for heating is another additional resupply headache. Naptha is the fuel normally used in tent or snow-hole heating and, if it is to be safe, it cannot be contaminated by other fuels. It has to be kept strictly segregated from them. A separate Naptha resupply chain has to be set up and this calls for more containers and the vehicles to lift them, and adds to the transport load.

For the maintenance function, working in the snow is horrid. Because of the constant running, vehicle maintenance is skimped by crews and more defects occur. This, coupled with the increase in vehicle accidents caused by bad driving conditions, means a high routine workload before even the effects of enemy action are taken into account. The mobile repair and recovery teams at 1st Line face the prospect of attempting repairs on damaged vehicles in sub-zero temperatures that will freeze unprotected flesh to bare metal. The 2nd Line workshops can work in heated conditions but this uses a lot of fuel. Trying to heat large vehicle hangars in these temperatures is difficult without special 'space' heaters and even then the temperature within the hangars can only be brought up to just above freezing. Once repaired, there is the danger that the repaired equipment will freeze-up as soon as it is taken outside; this is normally avoided by keeping the equipment running as it is taken outside. The repair of electronics is even more difficult. It best attempted in the warm but then has to be de-humidified before it can be taken outside. Overall, operating in the snow can double repair times.

The medical function faces problems which are almost, but not quite, the antithesis of those met in the desert. Instead of drugs and blood having to be kept cold, now they have to be prevented from freezing. Instead of heat-related malaises, the medics now meet cold-related injuries such as frostbite and hypothermia (when the body's core temperature falls below its life-sustaining level). Casualty evacuation in the snow is much more difficult than in the desert. Wheeled vehicle evacuation becomes slower than tracked vehicle and despite the bravery of their crews, weather conditions often prevent evacuation helicopters from getting to casualties. The only recourse is to move the dressing stations closer to the front, but still out of indirect fire range, and to accept that they might become 'fixed' for up to 10 days once they accept the badly wounded. But desert operations and operations in the snow do share the need for exemplary unit hygiene. Internal ailments can reduce unit efficiency and add massively to daily sick lists in both climates.

Mountain Operations

Arguably it is in the mountains that terrain constrains the logistician the most. Jungle presents its challenges because of limited resupply routes; but so do the constricted and vulnerable valley routes of the mountains. The desert has its heat and its rapidly changing temperatures; but in the mountains it can be equally dry. A soldier working hard and clad in protective clothing can reach very high body temperatures and face ambient temperature changes that are almost as great, and in many ways even more crippling. Elsewhere, the air dimension can help get the logistician out of trouble. But mountains are three dimensional and the air around them is thin, which has its effect on machines as well as men. Thus logistic support for mountain operations faces challenges which are almost a mixture of all those caused by every other type of terrain or climate.

Much depends on the time of year. The worst times are the spring and autumn when mountain weather can change from winter to summer, and back again, in the space of four hours. This is the most challenging period for the transport columns who, especially as they gain height, can meet dry tracks, then quagmires, followed by snow drifts. At least, if sufficient air defence assets are available to picket the heights around the main supply routes, the terrain ensures the air threat is less. This is welcome because convoy speeds will be much slower, as low as 15 km in the hour. Heavily-laden trucks will have to labour up inclines in a rarefied atmosphere in which their engines are never working to full efficiency. They will never be out of all-wheel drive and the lower gears. The wear and tear on drivers and vehicles will be considerable. Transport units will have only 60–70 per cent of their vehicles fit for duty at any one time.

Rather like in snow operations, conventional logistic unit siting maxims have to be abandoned and the criterion becomes, as it was for the Roman legionaries of old[5], not the distance between locations but the time taken to travel that distance. Modern transport units' mountain maps will be based on time and not distance. Logistic locations will need to be sited closer together, with 2nd Line units not more than 45 minutes away at the most from the front line units they support. In the mountains this can be as little as only 2km from the front line. But much depends on the availability of flat ground for storage sites. There are unlikely to be many of these and logistic units will occupy great lengths of the base of the valley, with a consequent increase in the time it takes to load and unload convoys.

The supply function faces a very unsatisfactory situation for its traditionally tidy mind. Soldiers will need access to hot weather, temperate weather and cold weather clothing, although not necessarily at the same time! Because of the temperature changes involved in mountain warfare, this takes some control. The British force sent to Norway in 1940 went prodigiously well equipped for mountain warfare. Unfortunately, all this issued clothing was very heavy and the initial temperatures in the fjord valleys were not all that cold, so the units either left their special clothing at the disembarkation port or abandoned it soon after; only to regret it when later they climbed higher into the mountains.

The priority for ammunition resupply remains with the shells for high-angle artillery (most armies have specialised light howitzers for mountain work) and for mortar ammunition. More types of fuses have to be carried to allow for the different climatic conditions. Fuel consumption increases for all vehicles and also for heating; mountain spring and autumn nights can be very cold. Separate fuel resupply chains have to be set up, very similar to those used in snow operations. In the summer, fresh food distribution becomes more difficult and, as in the desert, refrigerated containers have to be used. Water supply is only slightly less difficult than in snow operations and, above the snow line, is exactly the same, as are the precautions and remedies. Above all, the supply function depends on the speed with which the transport can replenish. This, matched with the expected combat rates, means that mountain warfare is particularly prone to the 'stop-go' pace which inevitably occurs when combat units cannot be replenished fast enough.

Above the snow line the repair function faces the same difficulties it faced for operations in the snow. Below the snow line the repair function is less affected by climate but, above and below it, in mountain warfare the recovery function becomes of vital importance. Such is the shortage of practicable routes in mountain warfare that the customary one good road and two reasonable tracks for a brigade becomes often one reasonable track for a division. Keeping this track clear of all breakdowns and accidents becomes vital for casualty evacuation and for the flow of supply to the division. Consequently, the recovery mechanics have to picket every likely choke point on the evacuation and resupply route, and there can be many of these. If necessary, recovery vehicles have to be taken away from divisional units to ensure that enough are made available to cover the route.

The medical function's prime challenge in mountain warfare is the speedy evacuation of wounded in time to meet the requirements of the Six Hour Rule, particularly from the point of wounding to the regimental aid post. Often the only way this can be done is by using stretcher-bearers. Evacuation from the regimental aid post to 2nd Line has its obvious difficulties, especially in the winter when snow and ice makes every journey perilous. Even the helicopter has difficulties in the high altitudes and bad weather. Moreover, altitude-related sicknesses have to be added to the catalogue of winter warfare injuries. This rather gloomy medical picture is partially offset by the fact that mountain warfare, although there are moments of intensive conflict, does not routinely produce the high casualty rates of other types of conflict. Thus for the medics, the greater number of difficulties is partially offset by the fact that they have less to do.

14.

Logistics 2000 Plus

It is inconceivable that any British government, of whatever political persuasion, would consider a Middle East military adventure in the future. The core of the United Kingdom's defence policy remains NATO and all resources should be devoted to this.[1]

The above quote supposedly dates from the middle 1980s. Four years later British soldiers were deploying to Saudi Arabia to take part in the liberation of Kuwait. Twice in one decade (the Falkland Islands and Kuwait) the United Kingdom went to war in areas of the world where it thought it never would. The quote shows, however, the inherent dangers that face anyone involved in trying to make military prophecies. The year 2000 of this Chapter's title is not far away. A civilian reader might be forgiven for wondering why, if it is so close, making military prophecies about the start of the new century should be so difficult. The main problem is that, almost more than in any other epoch, everything is changing. The almost 50-year-old Cold War global alliance patterns look likely to change or to break up. There are emerging nation states in Eastern Europe and what was the Soviet Union and, elsewhere in the world, others look likely to lose their superpower sponsors. All these nations are looking to establish themselves in some sort of military alliance framework. Arguably, the end of superpower rivalry has made the world a more dangerous place than it has been for half a century. More to the point, when everything is changing, there is no knowing where trouble will next spring up. Add to this that technology has an evolutionary rate all of its own. Armies are studying even smarter weapons. Around the corner could be a technological revolution that would make existing military hardware obsolete overnight. All this adds up to a possibly very dangerous period for the world and its inhabitants.

Even more importantly, the military in some Western countries have lost the comfortable and clear enemy that was the Soviet Union and its allies. It was this obvious and constant danger that made it easier for Western military men and their much maligned civil servant allies to justify the large amount of government funds spent on military forces and their equipment. It was this clear threat, especially localised and evident in Europe, that enabled Western military men to plan for a future war within strict parameters. This comfortable structure is no longer there.

It is customary in democratic countries to deplore expenditure on armaments as conflicting with the requirements of the social services. There is a tendency to forget that the most important social service a goverment can do for its people is to keep them alive and free.[2]

Despite Sir John Slessor's sentiments above, the 'end' of the Cold War means there is now a political grouping within almost every Western nation that is demanding a 'peace dividend'; the allocation of scarce government resources to programmes other than defence. As a result, almost without exception, Western nations are now demobilising. The United States has started a process of withdrawal from Europe, the United Kingdom is reducing its army by one third and this is reflected almost everywhere. Even France, a pragmatic and hard-headed nation when it comes to its own defence, is reducing. Thus, not only is the world becoming arguably a more dangerous place with potential trouble spots in almost every area of the globe, but the Western nations' ability to respond to such trouble is being reduced. All this makes conflict in the future more, not less, likely. The logistician's task will not change. It will continue to be the support of such conflict. The only sure thing is that there will be less logistic resources available to do so.

Yet this book started by advancing the thesis that there were certain logistic principles that, whatever the century or the place, have and will continue to be constants for any army.

First it must fight. Second it must eat. Third it must be capable of rapid movement. And last but not least, it must be equipped with all essentials necessary to the accomplishment of its mission.[3]

There will be conflict and it will need to be logistically supported. The basic facts of military life are that, to be able to fight, military forces must be able to move to the theatre of operations. Once in the theatre of operations armies, navies and air forces must be supplied with the basic necessities of war otherwise the campaign will be lost before it starts. Lastly, the logistic forces involved in the conflict must be structured to support combat and must be practised in that task, if the combat forces are not to find that their logistic support becomes a constraining, if not battle-losing, factor.

Moving to the Theatre of Operations

Some, for their subordinates, exasperating military commanders have as a catch phrase 'Expect the Unexpected'. Wherever future conflict occurs it is almost a certainty that it will take place in an area that at least one and possibly both, of the belligerents had not considered. One of the two sides involved will have to move great distances by sea and air to the theatre of operations.

There is a growing body of 'informed' opinion that the need to move far and fast reinforces a future requirement for light and airmobile forces which would be able to move swiftly to the danger area. Certainly there is a place for such forces because the political imperative will be to get round forces into the theatre of operations as quickly as possible. An arr   division that might take six weeks to arrive would clearly be insufficient for deterrence or to express national will. Some ground elements must be able to move swiftly to the crisis area. But to rely on such forces alone must surely be wrong. History abounds with examples of light forces meeting heavy ones. Unfortunately, in most cases victory went to the heavier side. The French 1940 *Division Legère* was light and highly mobile but, when they came up against the heavier German Panzer divisions, their speed and lightness did not help. Even with the armed helicopter, super weapons and air superiority, heavy armoured forces seem likely to be needed to attack, to seize and to hold ground. Future armies, if they are to be able to support their national policies, must be a mixture of light and heavy formations and the logistician must be prepared to support both.

Much has been spoken of the 'What If' factor, as in what if the Iraqi forces that seized Kuwait in August 1990 had just continued on into Saudi Arabia. Certainly, there was little to stop them. The bulk of Saudi oilfields could have been in their hands and the government of King Fahd might have fallen. The world knows that the West's reaction to the invasion of Kuwait was swift. In less than a week, US air and ground forces were in Saudi Arabia. Some 11 days after the invasion the US forces had grown to 25,000 and the first British elements (one squadron of Tornados and one squadron of Jaguars) had arrived. Even if the Coalition had not chosen first to exhaust the diplomatic and economic options, but had gone straight for a military solution, it would have taken a long time to build up the strength needed to defeat the main Iraqi forces in battle. The British Gulf forces, with the exception of the relatively few vessels of the Royal Fleet Auxilliary, relied almost entirely on hired civilian merchantmen. The US at least had their 'Ready Reserve Fleet'. But some of this fleet was reported to unserviceable or unseaworthy, understandable in an ancient and largely moth-balled force. Even with this fleet, the US had to hire vast amounts of civilian shipping. It was fortunate, particularly during the first 'defensive' phase, that the Coalition had the required amount of time and that the necessary logistic build-up could be made. Had Iraq continued its advance, the Coalition would have faced a very much more difficult task.

The Coalition forces were also fortunate that when their light forces arrived in Saudi Arabia they were not called upon to fight. If they had been forced to do so they would have had to engage in armoured high-intensity conflict for which they were not structured. Nor, on arrival, did they have enough logistics to be able to fight at intensive rates. The logistic units to make this possible could have been made available; but supplying the light forces in combat would have drastically reduced the amount of lift, especially airlift, available for the move to Saudi Arabia of the heavy follow-on forces. Something would have had to give.

The lesson for future campaigns is simple. Light forces alone will not be enough to meet every eventuality. Armies could return to the practice of vast strategic stockpiles dotted around the globe. The US has stocked the British island of Diego Garcia in the Indian Ocean and keeps ready-loaded ships anchored in its waters. For most nations this course is not open; cost and political feasibility preclude it. So the heavy forces that will almost certainly be needed will have to be moved into the area of conflict. When the time comes to move either light or heavy forces, the aircraft and shipping to move them will be scarce, especially heavy-lift aircraft. Nations serious about maintaining a credible future ability to project power and to wage war must either invest in fleets of strategic heavy-lift aircraft of the US C5 type and take steps to ensure they retain a national merchant marine, or make sure that they are allied to a nation with such assets, or ensure that they can be obtained from the civil sector. The UK currently favours the option of relying on civil assets. The US has gone for a blend of military and national self-sufficiency, with the gaps filled by international civil assets.

Much is sometimes made of the fact that future wars are unlikely to be fought by single nations but will inevitably be undertaken in co-operation with allies. While this might highlight the need for interoperability, the allied nations will be using their strategic lift to deploy their own forces. They are unlikely, except for the transportation of a politically significant token force, to move other nations' troops until their own have been shifted. To be certain, a nation has to have the ability to start moving its own forces and this means spending money on transport aircraft and naval transports. Such a plea for resources to be made available to naval and air services might seem strange in a book on land force logistics. But, unless these transport assets exist or can be found, ground forces cannot be delivered to, or supplied while in, the theatre of operations. Without this air and sea transport force, any deployment of ground forces has a political impact only and no independent military substance whatsoever, and thus would be worse than useless. The requirement would be enough air and maritime assets to deploy and support a force of an enhanced heavy division, and to support it for 30 days at intensive rates. Much depends on the distances from the home country, but an air fleet of some 30 Starlifter-type heavy-lift aircraft and air tankers to increase strategic range, and a maritime group of some 12–15 supply vessels with three or four petroleum tankers, would be the minimum.[4]

Providing the Basic Necessities of War

To wage successful war an army needs weapons and equipment, the men to man these and the ammunition and fuel to sustain them in action. It is, however, rare that any one nation posesses all these. Even the richest nations find it difficult to maintain strategic stockpiles of raw materials and fuel stocks. Even when such exist, they cannot be inexhaustible and there is an eventual reliance on others. Nor can these stockpiles meet every eventuality and almost inevitably it will be discovered that there is one crucial raw material that has not been stored. Even the relatively humble charcoal, used in the nuclear, biological and chemical filters of armoured fighting vehicles and personal respirators (Gas Masks), can achieve an unexpected prominence.[5]

It is rare to find a nation that has both the raw materials and the manufacturing capacity to produce all types of modern weapons. Many nations have
the ability to make small arms and light vehicles, and the means to make the
ammunition for these, but complex main battle equipments are normally
beyond them. Purchases have to be made abroad from one of the main
international arms-producing nations. While most nations make some effort
to buy reserve stocks of these equipments when they make their initial
purchase, these reserves are rarely adequate for modern war. This means
that the nation concerned is somewhat tied to the supplier and examples of
this dependence, and its affect on international diplomacy, abound. The most
notable example is Israel's dependence on the United States for its major
military equipments. Israel recognises this; hence its attempts to create, at
considerable cost to its national economy, its own indigenous arms industry.
That Israel has been partially successful is shown by its home-produced
Merkerva tank; but the cancellation of the Israeli Rafael fighter aircraft
project shows that even the most determined nation can rarely go it alone.

This reliance on others is accentuated by a growth in the cost of military
equipment. The expense of modern military equipment has led to a growth in
collaborative projects, where two or more nations join together to save costs
in designing and producing equipment. One of the best examples of this sort
of project is the Milan anti-tank missile. Produced by a number of European
nations, each manufactures a particular part of the missile: the body and the
wings come from one nation; the motor from another and the warhead from a
third. Thus, should any of these nations contemplate war, it has to have at
least the tacit support of the other two if it is to be able to build replacement
missiles.

Even those nations which have solved the raw materials and collaborative
problems face the fact that their defence industrial base is not geared for war,
but for peace. Even if the factories that produce the equipment are still open
and working, their production rates are geared to peace. They cannot expand
to wartime rates of production without lengthy warning and considerable
stockpiling of raw materials. What is even more likely is that, the original
'run' of equipment having been produced, the factory has retooled to produce
something else. This means it would take even longer to reproduce the
original equipment. Much is made of 'industrial surge capacity' by those who
seek to reduce the size of reserve equipment holdings. This is defined as the
ability of industry to increase its production rate from peace to war. Such a
capability might have existed in the past. But the complexity of modern
military equipment, the reduced number of defence contractors and reduced
raw material stockpiles and collaborative difficulties make such a capacity a
rare beast indeed. Historical examples seem to show that, while industry is
capable of a short spurt of production when the likelihood of operations is
imminent, once the on-hand materials are used up, it takes six months to a
year for industry to achieve full wartime production rates. If future wars are
to be short-lived affairs, and most recent conflicts have been relatively short-
lived, then this quick spurt of production might be enough, at least for those

that were not fought intensively. It would not be enough to sustain a lengthy full-scale conflict. Even the technologically simple provision of military clothing is affected. The British Army, despite the personal intervention of the Secretary of State for Defence and six months' preparation time, found it difficult to equip just one small division with desert clothing for the liberation of Kuwait in 1991.

In essence, an assured militarily-significant industrial surge capacity does not exist. Future armies, if they are to remain credible, must invest in even larger reserve stocks. Almost certainly they will not. Politicians will demand quick victories of military commanders, not only because of the adverse political and economic effects of a long war, but also because the military resources will not be there to enable a long war to be fought. If a quick victory cannot be won, and the political and national will exists to keep on fighting, future wars will be 'stop-go' affairs. Offensives will continue until they run out of resources. Then there will be a pause as stockpiles are built up and offensive action can start again. A quick glance at conflicts since 1945, with the notable exception of revolutionary wars, would seem to support this thesis. As 1945, and its resultant stockpiles, has faded into the past, wars have become shorter. Those very few that have gone on between two relatively matched opponents and where the national and political will existed to continue the conflict, such as the Iran/Iraq conflict of the late 1970s, have been very much 'stop-go' affairs. There are no signs that future wars will be any different; unless there is a quick victory for one side.

The 'Open' Battlefield of the Future

The inter-war British military theorist, J. F. C. Fuller, postulated that future war would be fought by mechanised armies fighting very much like a fleet at sea. The opening stages of the Second World War seemed to support this. The success of the German blitzkrieg certainly showed the capacity for manoeuvre of mechanised forces matched with the tactical application of airpower. But the bulk of German Second World War forces were foot-mounted infantry supported by horse-drawn artillery and supply columns. These reduced the speed and tempo of Panzer operations so that, while there might have been daring armoured thrusts, the overall tempo of operations was that of the marching rate of unopposed infantry. Opposition also slowed down the pace of operations. The daring armoured thrusts of both sides went the quickest, furthest and deepest when opposition was relatively light. The German thrust into France in 1940, the initial Axis successes of Barbarossa, Patton's US 3rd Army thrust from Normandy to the Rhine and Montgomery's British thrust from the Seine to Brussels all took place against light opposition and after an initial breakthrough had been made. Even as the Second World War went on, and the mechanisation of armies increased, especially on the Allied side, tank heavy formations remained in the minority and true mobile warfare in most cases eluded both sides.

Modern armies are much more mechanised than their Second World War forbears. Even current nominally 'infantry' units (and a modern army has very few such formations) have scales of transport that would have rated them as 'mechanised' in 1940.[6] Furthermore, modern military formations have three or four times the firepower of their Second World War antecedents and large numbers of wheeled vehicles to match. Yet, until the 1990s, it still seemed as if true mobile warfare was going to continue to elude Western armies. Although the likely theatre of operations, Western and Central Europe, had most of the geographic requirements for mobile warfare (flat plains, good roads, relatively open country and few large rivers), the size of the contesting sides meant that there would be, once mobilisation had taken place, a very high density of troops to ground. Unless the Warsaw Pact launched a surprise attack before NATO mobilised, mobile warfare could only happen once a breakthrough had been made. This explains NATO's fear of a Warsaw Pact surprise attack and the Warsaw Pact's preoccupation with achieving an overwhelming massive superiority at chosen breakthrough points.

The reductions in military strengths resulting from the 'peace dividend' have reduced the number, or density, of troops to ground. In some cases, regular formations have been changed to reserve, but in most cases, the collapse of the Warsaw Pact has been taken as a reason to demobilise formations entirely. The British Army plans to reduce its fighting strength from three armoured divisions and a partially mechanised division to one armoured division and one mechanised division.

Elsewhere in the world the change is not so obvious. Away from the troop densities of Western Europe it has still been possible to wage mobile warfare. The Arab/Israeli conflicts have been mobile wars as was the liberation of Kuwait in 1991. Thus, for Fuller's mobile warfare to be waged, full mechanisation and relatively low troop densities are required. These conditions exist throughout the world and perhaps soon will in Western and Central Europe. The combination of a political and economic need for a quick victory, the inability of nations to support high intensity conflict for any but short periods and the existence of the prerequisites for Fuller's mobile warfare all point to future wars being short, mobile and of a particularly high intensity. Supporting such a war will not be easy for the logistician.

Logistic Assets available 'for the Open Battlefield'

Reduced troop densities do not make the logistician's support task any easier. Modern weapons demand greater resupply rates than their predecessors. The numerical reduction in weapon systems will mean that they, especially the long-range weapon systems, will be used more often. The increased distances between units will mean that logistic resupply will have to travel further, and overall will deliver less as a result. There will be fewer logistic units to carry out this task. When armies reduce the great cry is to reduce the 'Tail' to save the 'Teeth'. In almost every army, logistic units are being reduced both in number and in size.

Whenever military organisations come under financial constraint, they tend to make disproportionate economies in the logistic services compared to the combat arms.[7]

In the British Army, there is a planned reduction in combat units of some 25 per cent. But British logistic units seem likely to be reduced by as much as 40 per cent. Civilian commentators on military affairs might be forgiven for being somewhat confused. Since 1945 they will have heard ministers of defence stand up and reassure their nations that the reductions being made will reduce the support area but will not affect operational readiness. The bemused commentators might be forgiven if they became somewhat dubious about such statements. Either the defence ministers are telling the truth, in which case the army concerned is guilty of profligate waste in having far too many logistic personnel; or the logistic personnel were actually needed, and what is proposed is not as good as that which existed before. The American military, with their gift for colourful English, have expressed the dilemma as: 'you can only cut the tail so far before you arrive at your own ass.'

Despite the complaints of the logisticians, the fact remains that in the future they are almost certainly going to have to do more with less, perhaps as much as 30–40 per cent less which leaves the question of how are they going to do this?

Logistic Support for 'the Open Battlefield'

The less dense battlefield of the future seems set to be much more logistically testing than current battlefields. At the moment, the logistician faces a seemingly simple task of moving supplies through relatively safe rear areas to the combat troops. The challenge for current Western logisticians is to guarantee a 24-hour continuous resupply and evacuation chain to combat units. Even if this resupply fails, the combat units have their own logistic holdings. They can survive until such time as the logistic umbilical cord is refastened and supplies flow through to them again. But the size of this integral logistic reserve has grown as the demands of modern war have grown. As much as 30 per cent of some modern armoured combat units are logistic and administrative assets. Customarily these assets are mounted in wheeled vehicles, vulnerable to enemy action and slow to move across country. On the future modern open battlefield this combat unit 'tail' will be a constraining factor. It will have to be defended against a swiftly manoeuvring enemy. Tracked vehicle cross-country tactical movement will have to be slowed to the speed of the labouring wheeled vehicles. If they could, 1st Line combat commanders would get rid of this logistic tail.

Indeed, it can be argued that it is only the military requirement to over-insure massively that requires so much logistic support to be at 1st Line. Modern fighting vehicles, like Fuller's fleets, carry much of their ammunition with them; but not, it must be said, great reserves of fuel. Mechanised Infantry Combat Vehicles, the mainstay of modern armoured infantry units, can carry up to 14 days' worth of ammunition at Combat rates within their turrets and hulls. Carrying this amount of ammunition means that these combat vehicles do not really need to be topped up continuously. Main Battle Tanks are in a similar position but carry less, about two-and-a-half days of ammunition. Of course, individual tanks or sub-units can be involved in actions that mean that they actually expend ammunition at a much higher rate than that allowed for by the planning guidelines. Still, there will be other fighting vehicles within the same unit that have not, and ammunition can be transhipped from one to the other.

Conversely, other factors might seem to argue that there should be more, rather than less, logistic support at 1st Line. The most difficult of all logistic operations has been the tactical movement of supplies from 2nd to 1st Line. At the other lines of logistic support the only danger, other than enemy air action, has been the driving habits of military drivers. On the more open battlefield the 2nd to 1st Line journey will become even more tactically difficult. The lack of troop density will create gaps between which enemy forces might slink. There will be no safe areas for the 2nd Line resupply convoys. In their soft-wheeled vehicles they are very vulnerable to even light enemy forces. The convoys will have great difficulty in getting through to the units they support. In the advance, this difficulty will be compounded by the tactic of combat commanders to by-pass relatively light opposition. But even 'light' opposition could stop unarmoured logistic traffic. A single enemy Mechanised Infantry Combat Vehicle has greater firepower than any company-sized logistic unit and its weapons out-range every weapon held by logistic soldiers. Unless logistic units are to be equipped with heavier weapon scales, combat units will have to be provided as escorts for the logistic convoys. Otherwise, the resupply will not get through, casualties will not be evacuated and the advance will falter.

If, to the changing tactical factors, one adds the requirement to reduce logistic numbers and resources at least commensurate with the reductions being planned for the combat units under the 'peace dividend', there comes the inevitable conclusion that there are going to have to be drastic changes in one, at least, of the four traditional lines of logistic support. But this book has tried to show that previous soldiers were no tyros in the art of war. They invented four 'field' lines of logistic support because four were needed. The difficulty then is deciding how the skeletons of these four lines of support can be preserved against the short-sighted military and civilian sharks that are now circling them. The balance to be struck is between the operational effect of a reduction and the amount of 'savings' that such a cut will bring. There may still be ways of 'shaving' the tail, provided that such a shaving has not taken place already. But with a 'tail' that has been reducing steadily since 1945, it probably has.

15.

Doing More with Less

The country must have a large and efficient army, one capable of meeting the enemy abroad, or they must expect to meet him at home.[1]

Wellington's words may relate to an earlier era but they are equally applicable to the present day. A very small military force, no matter how good, will almost always eventually succumb to a less good but larger enemy. The most difficult part of an army to create is its fighting element. Reliance can be placed on reserves but it has to be appreciated that these reserves will need time, historically at least six months or longer, before they can become 100 per cent effective on the field of battle. Nowadays the logistician, of all the types of military man, realises that an army's strength is derived from its manpower and equipment reserves. It would be a rare logistician who argued that an army should be all 'Tail' and no 'Teeth'. Equally, the thinking combat officer appreciate that a modern mechanised army cannot be all 'Teeth; and no 'Tail'. Such an army would grind to a halt after a few days.

Arguably, the 'Teeth-to-Tail' arguments are no longer applicable. A modern combat force is one whole, combat troops and logisticians. If peace dividend reductions in armies are to be made it could be that complete military formations should go; for it is in these formations that the bulk of a peacetime army's manpower lies. Reductions made in this fashion would be balanced. As the combat units left the order of battle then so would the logistic units that supported them. But modern armies will have few enough combat formations. The British Army currently has four divisions and a brigade and plans to have two divisions and a brigade. While it might be difficult to work up a battalion-sized unit for operations, it is doubly difficult to work up three such in an infantry brigade and trebly difficult to work up an all-arms formation. Yet all-arms formations are needed because modern warfare requires an orchestration of available combat means and it is only at the formation level that this orchestration can take place. Consequently, most logisticians would accept that, before further reductions are made in the combat arms and their formation headquarters, the resources devoted to logistics should be examined once more to see if there are areas where cuts in logistic strength can be made without too great an operational penalty.

Base Logistic Support in the Future

Some of the workshops and logistic depots and installations within the Base are not really needed in war. The depots holding ammunition stocks are a particularly good example of this. They hold the reserve stocks for operations. On mobilisation these depots are emptied as their contents are outloaded to the theatre of operations. It is unlikely that civilian industry would be able to gear itself up to fill these depots as fast as they were emptied. Indeed, subsequent production by industry is far more likely to be shipped direct to the theatre of operations. Thus the depots might be by-passed for all but quality control checks. Linked in with this is the fact that 3rd and 4th Line logistic unit will have little to store until the base depots have been outloaded. Consequently, it is quite feasible that the military in these depots could outload their stocks and, in the time it takes those stocks to get to the theatre of operations, the military could be flown out to meet them when they arrive in the combat area. Of course it is not as easy as this rather simplistic description would make it appear. There will be a need for reconnaissance parties to leave the depots early and there will still be a trickle of ammunition that needs to pass through the depots.

Similarly, in all but a very lengthy war, the huge Base workshops are going to find themselve with little work to do. Future armies are unlikely to have great reserves of equipment and, if there is a conflict, the bulk of an army's combat equipment will be deployed to the theatre of operations. So the Base workshops are rather like the ammunition depots, needed in peace but not needed so obviously in war. Unfortunately, the demands of the peace dividend are for reductions and financial savings in peace. One way round this problem might be the concept of 'Regular Shadow'.

If parts of the Base might not be needed in war there are two possible options. The first is to civilianise or contractorise them and remove the military element completely. Such a move saves the difference between the cost of the military and the cost of the civilians needed to replace them. This can add up to a lot of money over a lengthy period. However, the military and the nation are subsequently very vulnerable to the demands of the civilian contractor. The contractor could win the task with an initially very low bid. Once the military infrastructure is dismantled, the contractor can raise the cost of the services or ignore parts of his contract which reduce the profit margin, or both. The second way forward is to move soldiers from the field army into the depots and workshops to replace or supplement the civilian work force. On mobilisation, when the depots and workshops became largely moribund, the soldiers could move out to join the field army.

Overall, this concept of 'Regular Shadow' units has much to commend it, to both financiers and military men. For the financiers, instead of paying for two groupings, – some of the military at 3rd and 4th Line (that have little productive work to do in peace time) and a civilian work force in the workshops and depots (that might not be needed post-mobilisation) – only one grouping, the Regular Shadow units in the depots, needs to be paid. For the military men there is also an advantage. While it is true that regular units would be ideal, if these units existed there would be considerable difficulty in keeping their trade skills alive, because, with no peace logistic task, these skills could easily atrophy. Military skills could be kept alive by releasing the Regular Shadow units for exercises with their parent formations. Armies serious about their future logistic support might consider this Regular Shadow solution for the future.

Such an obviously beneficial system must have its flaws, and it does. The use of Regular Shadow saves money but it does not save on the overall number of soldiers. This alone might not meet the aspirations of those baying for a peace dividend; albeit that it can be argued that Regular Shadow soldiers actually save money. Then there is the fact that Regular Shadow soldiers should not be considered as just an amorphous mass. To send into battle soldiers that are not organised and trained as a military unit is criminal and a recipe for military disaster. So Regular Shadow units should be grouped together in peace with their own commanders and administration, and this increase their cost. In peace time it will seem to financiers that these commanders and trainers will be doing no useful work. Operationally, Regular Shadow units organised in this fashion would link in easily to an existing field unit, where the higher level operational planning and co-ordination tasks had been carried out for them. But, such is likely to be the push for savings from the logistic area, that these field army logistic unit headquarters and the few regular sub-units they command are highly likely to figure in any peace dividend cuts. Similarly, the Regular Shadow sub-unit headquarters will, to the financial eye, seem like unproductive overheads and establishment reviews will inevitably recommend their removal. With these regular skeletons gone either the unit headquarters in the field army or the sub-unit headquarters in the Base, the military argument for the use of Regular and the Shadow becomes less obviously operationally attractive and the sub-units are vulnerable to transfer to the reserve.

The assault on the Regular Shadow units does not just come from the front. The financiers will always quote that military manpower costs more than civilian to man logistic installations. Superficially this is true. The soldier brings with him costs in housing, pensions and administration that are greater than those of a civilian. Equally, the civilian will work full time in a workshop or depot and will not be taken away to go on exercise or military training and thus, on a straight one-to-one comparison, seems cheaper. But often this is not the case. The soldier is often younger and fitter than the civilian and is thus available for work more often. For the same reasons, the soldier is better able to respond to short notice 'surge' demands that occur when armies move from a peacetime to a wartime posture; what the British military call 'TTW' (Transition to War). Furthermore, experience shows that there is a limit to the amount of overtime that civilians are able, or willing, to work and this is particularly evident during lengthy periods of operation. There are some trades which are purely military and for which there is no civilian equivalent. There are others where the cost of a civilian tradesman is almost as much as a soldier, especially when other financial factors (over-time, unsocial hours, civilian manning regulations, civilian sickness rates) are involved. But, above all, there is the operational advantage of having Regular Shadow units.

4th Line in the Future

Of all the Lines of Logistic Support, it is 4th Line that is the most difficult to justify. So much depends on the infrastructure within the theatre of operations and the tactical situation. The liberation of Kuwait in 1991 was mounted from Saudi Arabia. There was a relatively sophisticated infra-structure, including a port, Al Jubayl, designed to handle huge surges in workload. Al Jubayl was built to handle the massive annual influx of *Haj* pilgrims to Mecca. Moreover Saudi Arabia, as one of the largest oil producers in the world, was awash with fuel. In many ways, Saudi Arabia was an ideal mounting base for the Kuwait operation. The same lavish infrastructure cannot be guaranteed for future campaigns.

The inescapable fact of logistic life is that there will always be a require-ment for the four lines of field logistic support. This does not, however, mean that the way in which support is provided at these lines cannot be changed. In most modern armies the result of peacetime reductions has all but civilia-nised logistic support at 4th Line, if it exists at all. In peacetime civilian facilities can meet this task and remove the need for military completely. In any military deployment the arrival of combat units can be supported by their own integral logistic units. Thus a brigade deploying will have its own logistic units to organise disembarkation and the storage around the point of entry. As the brigade moves off, divisional logistic units will arrive to take over the point of entry function. As the division moves off, corps logistic units will be arriving for this task. The real requirement for a separate 4th Line arises when the corps moves off to battle. Thus, as a generalisation, logistic 4th Line units are needed last of all. If risks have to be taken with logistic support, perhaps they can be best taken with 4th Line logistic support.

There are only three basic options open. The first of these is the abandon-ment of military units at this level of support and their replacement by a reliance on either the existing civilian infrastructure or by placing the responsibility for the functions at this line to civilian contractors. The terms of the contract would in some way require continued support, even in war. Reliance on civilian contractors has its obvious flaws.

> Waste and corruption by inefficient civilian contractors, principal among them in roguery the sutlers who sold food to the soldiers.[2]

Throughout history contractors have promised much but, 'when push of pike has come to shove', they have delivered little. Indeed, this is why logisticians were first put in uniform. The first problem is for the contractors actually to produce a work force in the war zone. The call-up of army reservists is always bedevilled by the fact that the personal circumstances of individual reservists change as time goes by. The, on discharge, single 24-year-old soldier becomes the father of a large family and the sole support of ageing parents by the time that mobilisation comes about. There is no reason to believe that civilian contractors' staff will not have similar excuses. As civilians are liable only to civil, and not military, law there is an even greater likelihood, despite signed contracts to the contrary, that the civilian worker will decline to serve in a combat zone. There is even less likelihood of the civilian worker continuing to honour his contract if 4th Line comes under any sort of enemy attack. The SCUD attacks on the 4th Line areas of the Coalition forces in the liberation of Kuwait, relatively few as they were, were rumoured to have caused a flurry amongst civilian contractors and a steady trickle out of the theatre of operations for various reasons.[3] Similarly, the French stevedores in the port of Calais 1940 abandoned the unloading of the British motor brigade's equipment after the first STUKA raid.[4]

The second method of achieving savings at this level of logistic support is to rely completely on reserves. 4th Line logistic tasks, in all the logistic disciplines, are the most similar to civilian tasks. Thus no great special training is needed and the requirement for the bulk of 4th Line assets to arrive later in a deployment makes this even more a reserve task.

The third, and obviously best, method is that 4th Line units should really be regular. But such a course is costly and almost certainly would not be taken. There is, however, some requirement for regulars at this line of support. 2nd Line field force logistic units are unlikely to have skilled quayside crane operators for example, and this sort of skill will be needed right at the start of any campaign.

Future 4th Line support will probably be provided by an amalgam of all these three courses. There will be regulars for the command and control and planning functions and for those logistic tasks which need to be done from the start. There will be reserve units for those aspects, like the medical function, where civilian contractors are unavailable or inappropriate. There will be civilian contractors for those functions where the requirement is either so particularly specialised (like some electrical or optical repairs) or is so general (like the provision of catering services or labour support) that contractors will be the obvious choice. It is in the field of the very specialised repair functions that the a reserve liability for civilian contractors might be particularly necessary.

Although such a hybrid system can be made to work – it was very much how the US forces in the liberation of Kuwait organised their 4th Line Logistic support – future planners need to appreciate that it is not ideal. It might work well when the side concerned is winning, but its true test would be if the side concerned was losing and the 4th Line area became subject to attack. In such conditions history abounds with contractors who failed to live up to their contracts or whose workforce fled when under attack. The use of contractors is very much a worst case solution and any planner that believes otherwise is deluded, and is deluding the nation for which the plan has been made. But it is almost inevitable that it will happen. It saves money.

Future 3rd Line Logistic Support

The quest for savings is likely to hit logistic support at 3rd Line as well. The use of civilian contractors is less obviously right. This close to the enemy the requirement for trained and organised military logistic units is self-evident. Indeed, the proximity of the enemy and the likelihood of enemy action argues for nothing less than regular military units. But, again, it is highly unlikely that sufficient resources will exist to have such units. For those seeking to justify 3rd Line logistic units the problem is compounded by the fact that, in peacetime, this level of logistic support is rarely needed; it is often quicker and cheaper to deliver directly to 2nd Line or 1st Line units from the Base. Thus, in peacetime, if 3rd Line units were to be all regular, they would be doing no work other than to train for their wartime task. Such a concept is not alien to armies. After all, this is exactly what combat units do in peacetime. But for some reason the same logic is rarely applied to logistic units. Instead, the reliance of most armies on reserves for the 3rd Line logistic task is most marked.

There is some justification for this. Although closer to the enemy and the likelihood of enemy action than 4th Line logistic units, at 3rd Line the enemy is still some way away. Thus the initial level of military training of reserve units might not need to be as high as their regular counterparts. Similarly, the size of the technical function at this level of logistic support is such that it lends itself to single commodity or function sub-units. Generally, this is a simpler technical task than that facing the multi-commodity or multi-function units further forward. This means that reserve units could well be considered for this line of logistic support; but not exclusively. The reserve units still need a regular leavening of command and control. Additionally, some regular sub-units are needed to support initial deployment and to be there to meet the start of the build-up of the 3rd Line reserve stocks.

The 3rd Line medical units are particularly important to an army at war. Civilian installations this close to the enemy are unlikely to have spare capacity to handle military casualties; if that is, the civilian hospitals exist in the first place. Not all nations are as well endowed with medical facilities as those in Western Europe. The Regular Shadow concept is particularly useful at this line of support. The doctors and medical staff from the Base hospitals can be used to form the basis of some of the field and general hospitals that will be needed. Reserve hospitals could then fill-in as required. Unfortunately, the Base hospitals are likely to be just the sort of logistic installation that might have already been cut to make savings and, depending on the army concerned, might not exist. Reserve units could be used exclusively at this level but, again, any programmer who planned on this should acknowledge that it is very much a less than ideal concept and that medical support to the combat soldier might not be as good as it should be.

Future 2nd and 1st Line Logistic Support

Continued reductions in the Base and at 4th and 3rd Line are unlikely to come up with the size of reductions being demanded for the peace dividend. Many of the measures that might produce savings have already been taken in the long logistic decline since 1945, so there is not a lot of logistic 'fat' to be cut out of 3rd and 4th Line and the Base. About the only lines of logistic support which still have large numbers of regular logistic manpower are 2nd and 1st Line. It is at these lines of logistic support that the requirement for regular manpower is the clearest and the linkage between logistic units and the supported combat formations the most obvious. Thus even combat commanders have joined the fight against any proposed reductions to what they see as 'their' logistic units. This is a rather simplistic view because it ignores the fact that logistic support is one chain from the Base to the front line. Like a chain, logistic support is only as good as its weakest link. To have a logistic chain with one strong link invites the conclusion that, under stress, one of the other links will snap and the chain of logistic support will be broken.

Paradoxically, the advent of the Open Battlefield forces a reappraisal of the traditional methods of support to combat forces and this reappraisal could provide the reductions for which planners are looking, and without great operational detriment. On the Open Battlefield the traditional resupply convoys from 2nd to 1st Line are very vulnerable and it is arguable whether they would, in fact, get through to the units they are supporting. Conversely, unit commanders do not want to be saddled with an immobile 1st Line logistic tail. There are two stark alternatives; either 1st or 2nd Line logistic support has to be drastically reduced.

The arguments for the abandonment of 1st Line support are that future combat commanders cannot be tied by the need to drag a sizeable and restraining logistic tail around the battlefield. The tanks and mechanised infantry combat vehicles of the combat units carry a considerable amount of ammunition; often sufficient to fight for one or two days at high intensity rates. Because of this, they do not need continuous resupply. Their reserve ammunition holdings could be reduced to just that needed for dire emergencies. Instead, rather like naval vessels at sea, the combat units could come back to replenish at a supply point provided by 2nd or 3rd Line logistic units. The combat formations will be moving so fast that lengthy mechanical repairs just could not be made before the combat unit moves off. Thus the fighting units need not have the large repair sub-units and their associated stores carrying vehicles that they have now. The only maintenance vehicles required at 1st Line would be the recovery vehicles needed to return vehicle casualties to a more static and secure 2nd or 3rd Line repair site. Just the adoption of this measure would reduce the size of most British Army combat units, by about 15 per cent. There is little scope for the reduction of 1st Line medical assets. Because of the Six Hour and Ten Day rules, these are almost already configured for the mobile battle. The evacuation ambulances could, however, be grouped at the brigade level and the treatment facilities held at the divisional level.

Provided sufficient logistic support existed at 2nd Line, the sum of these reduction measures to 1st Line logistic functions would reduce the logistic tail of a modern combat unit by as much as 50 per cent. It is at the unit level that the most peacetime regular manpower exists and a reduction at 1st Line would accomplish the most 'savings'. Put simply, there is proportionately more regular logistic manpower at this level than anywhere else. So a reduction at this level produces the most savings.

This debate ignores the fact that 70 per cent of the logistic lift of an armoured division at war is devoted not to the direct combat units but to the artillery. Significant reductions in the transport lift devoted to artillery ammunition can only be made if the guns are going to fire less. But all the evidence is that they are going to want to fire more, both because of the improvements in the weapons themselves (which enables ammunition to be fired faster) and because of the increased use that will be made of artillery on the Open Battlefield (to fire into gaps and to lay artillery delivered mine-fields). Thus there is little likelihood of being able to reduce the amount of artillery ammunition that will need to be fired in war.

But modern artillery tactics very much lend themselves to the 'Shoot and Scoot' deployment of artillery. The guns move into position, fire, and then withdraw rapidly to avoid counter-bombardment. When the guns withdraw there is no reason why they should not return through an ammunition resupply point to restock their turrets and limber vehicles. If this procedure were to be followed, the requirement for the guns to have regular transport units in support of them decreases. The stocking of ammunition resupply points in an area to the rear is perhaps a task that can be left safely to the reserves. Thus the requirement for regular transport manpower in peacetime would no longer exist and considerable savings might result. But this trans-fer of a regular task to the reserve should not mask the fact that the transport task vehicles will be needed in war, and thus that the equipment for them has to be built and held in peacetime.

But reducing the logistic load on 1st Line must mean that, to some degree, the load is shifted to 2nd Line. This is not the completely the case. Having logistic assets with combat units is sometimes wasteful. A combat unit in reserve will not be fighting and thus it will have no need to be replenished. Its ammunition-carrying vehicles, more often than not, then stand idle, as do its fuel tankers. Grouping these assets centrally means they can be used more efficiently and therefore there will either be a greater in-built redundancy, or savings can be made in the number of vehicles. The question, though, is where they should be grouped.

The arguments are well balanced. If 2nd Line logistics are grouped at the brigade level (see Figure 15.1) then the combat commanders will have them as part of their formation. Most commanders would rather have this than have them in the gift of another. But as the future manoeuvre unit of modern armies seems likely to be the armoured brigade, this would still mean that

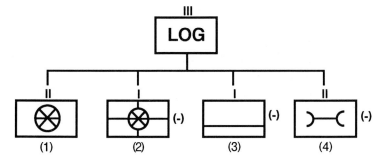

1.   This needs to be a very large transport battalion of a
company for each artillery battery supported and large platoons for
each combat unit.   Between 600 - 800 task vehicles and 1,500 to
2,000 men would be needed.

2.   Evacuation only. No treatment facility.

3.   Conversely, with so much stock carried on wheels, the
number of supplies used to store ground loaded commodities can be
reduced. The supply unit would just have stock controllers and a
mobile vehicle mounted materiel platoon.

4.   This maintenance unit has to have a depth repair facility as
well as a roadside repair facility. This could mean in the order of
100 - 150 vehicles and 400 men.

FIG. 15.1 Future brigade logistics?

the tactical commander would be constrained by a relatively slow-moving
and vulnerable logistic tail. Grouping logistics with brigades can be as
inefficient as grouping it with units. A brigade could be in reserve or not
heavily committed and its logistic assets would be relatively idle. A brigade
that had to undergo reconstitution would need help. But if logistics were
brigaded this help would have to come from other brigade commanders who
would be less likely to release logistic assets in war than they were in
peacetime map exercises. There are some units that clearly should not be
brigaded. No medical treatment facility, once it had taken in casualties,
would be immediately able to follow its brigade as it moved off for the next
operation. Treatment facilities would have to be commanded at the divisional
level with the evacuation ambulances grouped, more often than not, with the
brigade they routinely support. Lastly, no brigade will ever be truly self-
sufficient. There would almost always be something it lacked and needed
from the rear. But, if all 2nd Line assets were with the brigades themselves,
there would be nobody to deliver it.

Grouping all the logistic assets at the divisional level is undoubtedly the
most efficient use of them (see Figure 15.2). This would also mean they could
be best directed to meet the divisional commander's overall plan. But to
group them at this level puts logistic resources some way away from the units

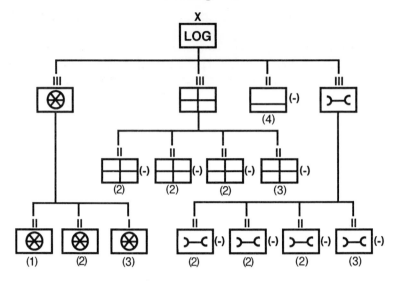

1.   For artillery resupply. This would be a very strong 1200 man battalion.

2.   Brigade support.

3.   Support to divisional troops.

4.   With so much on wheels, the requirement to ground dump stocks becomes less. Thus this battalion can be much reduced in size.

FIG. 15.2 Future divisional logistics?

they are to support. This adds to the reaction times for logistic units to respond to requests from fighting units.

The alternative is to do away with 2nd Line support and to leave combat units with a large logistic tail that enables them to be self-sufficient for up to five days. 3rd Line logistic units would set up reconstitution areas to which brigades would return for units to replenish when holdings were expended. This solution is very similar to that adopted by the Second World War German army to support their armoured formations on the mobile battlefield of the Eastern Front. The advantages of this method would be that the units of brigades would have assured logistic support under their own control and 3rd Line logistic units would have the relatively simple task of stocking a reconstitution area. The disadvantage is that combat units would still be tied to a slow and vulnerable logistic tail and it is this logistic tail which combat commanders believe will be an unduly constraining factor on the Open Battlefield of the future. To enable fighting to take place at the predicted rates, this tail would have to be very large indeed and there would be no guarantee that it would be large enough. There is always some spare part that is not carried or some ammunition nature that is fired more than any other.

It could be argued that the ideal solution would be to have logistic support at every level. But this ignores the tactical imperatives of the Open Battlefield and the financial imperatives of providing a peace dividend. All armies are considering the same problem. Probably as many solutions will be chosen as there are armies. Perhaps the best solution might be a hybrid of brigade and divisional logistics (see Figure 15.3).

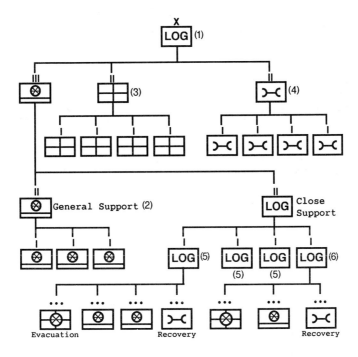

1.   A proper logistic headquarters and not a double earmarked staff officer in divisional rear headquarters.

2.   Primarily for artillery ammunition resupply but also available for engineer barrier plans and dumping tasks.

3.   Sub-units are medical treatment facilities only, no evacuation ambulances.

4.   Sub-units are repair units only, no recovery assets.

5.   Available for tasking to brigades. Including evacuation ambulances and recovery vehicles as well as normal supply and transport functions.

6.   For divisional troops support.

FIG. 15.3 The best, or the worst, of both worlds?

chosen as there are armies. Perhaps the best solution might be a hybrid of brigade and divisional logistics (see Figure 15.3).

In this solution the logistic assets of combat units, especially their ammunition lift and repair capacity, are much reduced. Logistic assets are centralised at divisional level where they can most efficiently be controlled but there is the capability to deploy to brigades a small logistic company-sized unit to serve as an immediate reserve. Additionally, the headquarters of this company could provide the logistic command and control focus for the needs of the brigade. It is this headquarters that would control the brigade's rear area and act as the focal point for resupply in, and casualty evacuation out, and might be the unit chosen to run the brigade reconstitution area. It would have no repair capability, because repair can be done better in centralised divisional workshops. It would, however, control a back loading point where unit recovery vehicles would drop off vehicle casualties and from which divisional vehicles would carry away the casualties. The company would have evacuation ambulances but no other medical facility. If it had any, it would become fixed as soon as casualties were taken in. A medical dressing station might be placed under command for a specific operation but would be left behind as the brigade moved off to the next action. The divisional artillery would have its own small transport regiment devoted to just artillery ammunition resupply and this could easily come from the reserves.

Such a solution would recognise the tactical realities of the Open Battlefield and the financial realities of the search for a peace dividend. There will never be enough logistic assets to satisfy the needs of modern war. The key is to have logistic command and control mechanisms in place on mobilisation to be able to make the best use of those logistic assets that are available. Military planners, financiers and politicians ignore this at their peril.

> In fact the battle is fought and decided by the Quartermaster before the shooting begins. The bravest men can do nothing without guns, the guns nothing without plenty of ammunition, and neither guns nor ammunition are of much use in mobile warfare unless there are vehicles with sufficient petrol to haul them around.[5]

Glossary

ABBOT UK 105mm self propelled howitzer.

ABRAHAMS US Main Battle Tank. Armed with a 105mm tank cannon in the M1A1 version and with a 120mm smooth-bore tank gun in the M1A2 version.

Airborne Operations. Operations involving the use of parachute troops.

Airmobile Operations. Operations involving the use of helicopter borne forces.

Advance To Contact. When one military force moves towards another but is uncertain of the enemy force's location. *See* **Transitional Operations**.

Air Dropped. Personnel or materiel dropped from aircraft or helicopters mainly using parachutes. But materiel can sometimes be dropped from very low level without using parachutes.

Air Landed. Strictly, personnel and materiel deployed to a theatre of operations by aircraft. Now growing to become a generic term to describe all operations involving aircraft, parachutes and helicopters.

Air Movement. Used to describe the deployment of military personnel and freight by aircraft.

All Wheel Drive Vehicles. Wheeled vehicles that have each of their wheels powered. Such vehicles have a much greater mobility than their conventional cousins and are the only logistic vehicles, other than the very rare tracked logistic replenishment vehicles, capable of even trying to keep up with armoured forces. Originally they were very expensive, both in financial and maintenance support. The growth of a civilian market in *Off-roading* has reduced both costs.

Ammunition Rates and Scales. 'Rates' are the amount of ammunition a weapon system can fire in a given period of time. Customarily armies have 'Intensive', 'Normal' and 'Low' rates of fire. Intensive rates of fire cannot be fired continually, both the weapon system and the crew can only keep this rate of firing for a limited time before fatigue sets in and the rate of fire drops. 'Scales' are the amount of ammunition given to a particular weapon system. They are normally linked to the type of conflict envisaged: High Intensity; Medium Intensity and Low Intensity. The old style 'Soviet' Red

Army took scales, which they called 'Units of Fire', one stage further and, based on historical evidence, produced the amount of ammunition needed to be fired at a particular piece of ground to achieve a desired effect (battlefield 'shock', killing and neutralisation). In the Soviet Army these were called 'Norms'.

Amphibious Operations. Military operations involving the disembarkation of personnel and materiel from water (sea, lake or river) to land without using a conventional port.

Armoured Recovery Vehicles. *See* **Recovery Vehicles**.

Asset Tracking. The increasingly important need to keep track of vital materiel in the resupply system. Such tracking can help reduce stockpile costs and reaction times but has some penalty in the terms that it is doing more with less. Thus, if something goes wrong with the asset tracking system, there is unlikely to be any 'spare' in the pipeline to make good an urgent operational demand. With the increasing costs of materiel it is unlikely that the finance would be available to maintain the vast reserve stocks of yester-year and the asset tracking route is probably the only one for the armies of the future.

Attrition. In military terms the degradation of a force, weapon or equipment system so that it operates at less than peak efficacy. Such attrition can be caused by enemy action, climate or usage.

Availability. *See* *RAM – D*.

Bar Coding. A system for putting all the information about something on a strip of paper that can then be read electronically. In use by almost every modern supermarket but not yet fully adopted by the military; largely because of the hardware costs involved. It can be used for the resupply chain and by movements experts and can revolutionise the passage of logistic information swiftly and accurately. It is a vital component of asset tracking systems.

Base, the. The grouping of the home-based military installations and civilian factories and industrial infrastructure which goes to make up the vital 'Base' on which logistic support is based and without which logistic support cannot be guaranteed. Many armies are 'paper tigers' in that they have no Base. Whilst they might have an impressive array of field hardware, without the Base to sustain them they rapidly become operationally ineffective. Armies with no Base are known as 'Shop Window' armies because everything they have is on display and there is nothing in the storeroom which can generate more.

Base Ammunition Depot. An ammunition depot in the Base. They normally hold all the war reserve stocks because even the greatest industrial nations would have difficulty in moving from peacetime production rates to those production rates needed to support modern war.

Base Hospital. A hospital in the Base. Traditionally these held the long term sick and wounded and provided rehabilitative care. Nowadays, few such military hospitals exist and reliance is placed on the nation concerned's civilian medical infrastructure; which in many cases might not be able to cope with the military load and its civilian load at the same time.

Base Materiel Depot. These depots, despite a widespread misconception, do not hold vast stocks of fast moving spare parts and materiel. Although in peace it is the fast moving spares that interest military commanders, the fact that they are fast moving means that normally there is a civilian production line set up in peace to supply the items. For the fast moving spares these depots act merely as the receipt point from the civilian factory into the military resupply system. More often than not, the bulk of the holdings of Base materiel depots are the spare parts for 'one-time buy' military special equipments, for which the factory production line will have closed down, and the reserve materiel stocks for cadreised units and for the limited war reserve stocks that an army is able to afford.

Base Postal Depot. The link between the military postal service and its civilian equivalent. Normally located at the communications nexus for the country concerned but, as this probably means expensive real estate, most armies are now being forced by their financiers to vacate these prime and valuable sites.

Base Repair Workshop. Where very complex and large overhauls and repairs are made to complex military equipment. As national industrial infrastructures grow more sophisticated, and as the equipment itself becomes even more esoteric and complicated, these workshops are being abandoned and the equipment repaired or overhauled by the civilian manufacturer or a contractor.

Base Vehicle Depot. A vehicle depot in the base which holds the reserves of vehicles for war and runs the resupply system for peacetime operating stocks.

Battle Attrition Studies. A generic term used to describe almost every armies' attempt to estimate what losses they might sustain in any future conflict.

Battle Fatigue. The lightest medical condition resulting from **combat stress**. Caused by tiredness and lack of sleep and normally remedied by a short period of rest out of the direct battle.

Battle Shock. A medical condition resulting from **combat stress**. Could be caused by a reaction to the numbing effects of a concentrated bombardment or direct hit on the equipment being manned.

Battlefield, Open. Handy description of the likely battlefields of the future which could have a lesser troop to ground ratio than that of likely NATO/ WARSAW Pact confrontations and thus might increase the likelihood of manoeuvre.

BERGEPANZER STANDARD. German Army tracked recovery vehicle.

'Black Boxes'. The term used by soldiers to describe the sealed, very complicated, **Line Replaceable Units** full of micro-circuitry that now form part of most main military equipments. 'Black' because it is alleged that the repair mechanic that replaces it has little idea of how it works and could not repair it with the tools he has even if he did.

BRADLEY. Most modern US Mechanised Infantry Combat Vehicle. Carries the lowest manoeuvre unit of an infantry platoon but the vehicle itself is armed and capable of fighting whilst the infantry are still within it or when they have dismounted.

BV 202. A Swedish tracked oversnow vehicle in service with a number of armies. Bring replaced by a newer model, the BV206.

Cadreisation. The word used to describe the practise of manning a military unit with less than its full establishment of regular soldiers. The difference is made up from the reserves upon mobilisation.

Casualty Estimates. The estimate by tactical commanders of how many casualties they might expect to suffer during a particular operation. The result depends on ratios of attackers to defenders modified by weapon, tactical and state of training factors.

Catering Function. The provision of food and its serving to the military.

CH 53. German Army medium lift helicopter.

CHALLENGER. UK Main Battle Tank

CHINOOK. US produced Medium Lift Helicopter in service with many armies around the world.

Combat Logistic Area. The area immediately to the rear of the combat troops where 1st and 2nd Line logistic support is provided.

Combat Stress. The generic term used to describe what used to be called shell-shock. *See* **Battle Fatigue** and **Battle Shock**.

Combat Holdings. The logistic stocks that every army unit carries. Normally a product of the operational task facing the unit concerned modified by the number of vehicles allocated to carry the stocks.

Company Aid Post. The first port of call for a casualty in a combat unit. Normally one or two vehicles with 4 to 8 men.

COFFER UK Army Field Computer System for materiel.

Container. The large metal boxes seen on the back of most civilian trucks. The dimensions of these have been standardised by the International Standards Organisation (*ISO*) and, in almost a silent revolution, they are now in general use within most armies.

Container Ships. Ships built to handle just ISO containers.

Counter Revolutionary War Operations. The term used by the military to describe what might have been described as civil wars before had it not been for the involvement of ideology. It describes a range of conflict from small scale banditry to full high intensity operations.

Defensive Operations. One of the NATO defined phases of war.

Delaying Operations. One of the NATO defined phases of war.

Demountable Loads. A description of a concept where a vehicle can off-load and pick up its own cargo body bed; instead of just its cargo. The concept allows much faster logistic vehicle turn-round times and is now being introduced, to most western armies under various acronyms (France – *VTL*, Germany – *MULTI*, UK – *DROPS*, US – *PLS*).

Dispatching Parachute Loads. Launching parachute loads out of aircraft and helicopters so that they arrive in a usable fashion on the ground.

Drop Zone. The area of ground where parachute forces and their logistic support are dropped.

DROPS. The UK 'Demountable Rack Off-Loading and Pick-Up System'. See **Demountable Loads.**

Durability. *See RAM–D.*

EAGER BEAVER. UK Army rough terrain fork lift truck.

ELEFANT. Historically a Second World War German self propelled anti-tank gun. The name has been carried forward into the modern-day German army as the description of the Germany army standard tank transporter.

Field Hospitals. 3rd Line hospitals which together go to make up the forward surgical complex.

First Line Logistic Support. Integral unit logistic support.

Fourth Line Logistic Support. Theatre-level logistic support. Confusingly, elements of Base logistic support might be brought forward to be included in this line.

Functions of Logistics. The division of logistics into supply, transport, maintenance, medical and the smaller functions of catering, post and labour.

General Hospitals. 4th Line hospitals of about 800 beds with all the facilities one would expect of a well equipped civilian hospital. They provide the long-term nursing and rehabilitation for casualties too sick to be sent back to the national base.

High Intensity Operations. A generic term used to describe 24-hour operations where almost every available weapon system is being used to its maximum effect and at its maximum rate.

Interoperability. The term used to describe when, although equipments are not the same, they can still work together. Thus, if a French fuel tanker made by Renault meets a German fuel tanker made by Opel, the contents can be transferred because the couplings have been standardised.

Isolated Operations. The operations of a military force when it has been cut off from its source of resupply. *See* **Transitional Operations**.

Jerrycan. The 20 litre fuel canister used by almost every army.

LEOPARD. The German Main Battle Tank. The *LEOPARD 1* has a 105 mm rifled tank gun and the *LEOPARD 2* a 120 mm smooth-bore gun.

Line Replaceable Units. *See* **Black Boxes**.

Lines of Communication. The logistic umbilical cord that stretches from the national Base to the theatre of operations and up to 1st Line.

Lines of Logistic Support. The division of logistic support to armies based on the type of task undertaken. *See* **First Line, Second Line, Third Line, Fourth Line** and **Base**.

Link-Up Operations. Operations by a military force to break through to a unit or formation that has been cut off. *See* **Transitional Operations**.

Local Purchase. Buying things in the theatre of operations rather than importing them from the national Base.

Logistic Planning Guide-lines. The culmination of **Attrition Studies** and **Reviews of Rates and Scales** which are turned into these guide-lines for logistic planners as to what their force will need in combat.

M1. See ABRAHAMS.

Main Supply Routes. The basic road framework for the logistic support of a military force. Known as *MSR*s in the UK and US armies.

Maintainability. *See RAM-D.*

MRE. MEAL READY TO EAT. US Army combat ration.

Mechanical Handling Equipment. Labour saving equipment such as fork lift trucks, pallet loaders and small cranes. Known as *MHE* in the UK and US armies.

Meeting Engagements. When two mobile forces meet each other. *See* **Transitional Operations**.

MEXE FLOAT. A UK ship to shore lighter used in amphibious operations.

MULTI. German Army demountable load system. *See* **Demountable Loads**.

'*Norms*'. The Red Army planning guide-lines for what force and resources are needed to achieve a particular tactical aim.

Operational Ration Packs. Pre-cooked meals issued to armies to reduce the time taken in cooking and to ensure that the soldier gets the right daily calorific intake for the theatre of operations concerned.

Passage of Lines. When one force passes through another of the same side. Divided into Rearward and Forward passage of lines. *See* **Transitional Operations**.

Phases of War. An attempt by the military to break-up warfare into readily understandable segments. The phases of war are defined by NATO as Defensive Operations, Offensive Operations and Delaying Operations.

PLS. The US demountable load system. *See* **Demountable Loads**.

Pull Tactical Combat Distribution. When logistic resupply is based on unit requests being passed back to the next line of logistic support.

Push Tactical Combat Distribution. When logistic resupply is based on standard resupply loads being passed forward to the next line of logistic support.

RAM-D. A maintenance acronym built-up from Reliability (how often an equipment will break down), Availability (how quickly the equipment can be returned to service), Maintainability (how easy an equipment is to fix) and Durability (how hard an equipment is to break).

Rail Transfer Equipment. Equipment introduced to speed the off-loading of demountable racks from railway wagons to demountable rack vehicles.

Ramp Powered Lighter. A UK self propelled ship to shore lighter used in amphibious operations.

Rear Logistic Area. The area in which 4th Line logistic support is found. *See* **Fourth Line**.

Rearward Passage of Lines. *See* **Passage of Lines**.

Reconstitution. The process by which military formations are restored to their previous combat power. There are three main methods: **Reorganisation; Redistribution**; and **Regeneration**.

Recovery. The maintenance task of collecting broken-down equipment and taking it off a route or to a repair workshop.

Recovery Vehicles. The tracked and wheeled vehicles especially designed to recover broken-down equipment.

Redistribution. The breaking-up of a unit that has suffered serious personnel and equipment casualties and the allocation of what is left to other units or formations. *See* **Reconstitution**.

Reliability. *See* ***RAM-D***.

Regeneration. Bringing a unit that has suffered serious personnel and equipment casualties back up to strength by providing it with replacements. *See* **Reconstitution**.

Reorganisation. Reorganising a badly mauled unit so that there are stronger, but fewer, sub units within it. *See* **Reconstitution**.

Red Army. The army of the former Soviet Union.

Regimental Aid Post. The battalion level field medical facility. Customarily a small platoon with a doctor and some six to eight vehicles.

'Regular Shadow'. The concept by which logistic soldiers are employed in the Base in peace but earmarked for operational deployment in times of tension and war; thereby saving some of the Base civilian workforce costs that would otherwise arise. Also known as 'Two for the price of One'.

Reliability. *See* ***RAM-D***.

Relief in Place. When one military unit or formation relieves another that is in contact with the enemy. *See* **Transitional Operations**.

REMUS. A very expensive German Army electronic repair vehicle.

Reviews of Ammunition Rates and Scales. Armies guesses as to how much ammunition they will be able to fire from each weapon system and how much is needed to arrive on the target to have the desired operational effect. Along with **Battle Attrition Studies** this tells armies how much ammunition they need to supply.

Rigging Loads. The specialised preparation of loads to be dropped by parachute.

Rough Terrain Container Handling Equipment. Mechanical Handling Equipment that can take containers and carry them across country.

Routine Combat Holdings. The logistic stocks a unit or formation would be routinely expected to have as a reserve against resupply being interrupted.

Speed of Reinforcement. The operational level movement of units and formations as formed bodies so that, on arrival, they are instantly ready to fight. This method is wasteful in transport assets.

Speed of Movement. The operational level movement of units and formations in the most efficient manner; which means that it might be some time before the units and formations can be assembled ready for action.

Second Line Logistic Support. The brigade or divisional level of logistic support.

Six Hour Rule. The historically proved medical rule that a casualty brought to surgery within this time has the greatest chance of recovery.

Specialised Operations. Operations requiring special techniques and organisations such as airmobile operations.

Standardisation. Agreeing to use agreed dimensions and similar criteria to ensure that, although equipment might be different, the same ammunition, fuel or even batteries can be used. Used to help in **Interoperability**.

Standing Operating Procedures. *SOPs.* The military system to simplify warfare by using common operating procedures and practices.

Stockpile Planning Guide-lines. *SPGs.* The planning guide-lines given to NATO nations as to what reserves of ammunition and equipment should be held.

STUFT. Shipping Taken Up From Trade. A UK term to describe merchant shipping hired to transport military forces.

SUPACAT. A UK all-terrain amphibious unarmoured light vehicle. For use by amphibious, parachute and airmobile forces.

Tactical and non-tactical loading. Tactical loading is the loading of ships and aircraft so that the last things loaded are the first things needed on arrival. Non-tactical loading is the loading of ships and aircraft in the way that makes the most efficient use of the space available.

Tank Transporters. The military term for a tractor unit and heavy lift trailer that can carry a main battle tank.

Ten Day Rule. The historically proven medical rule that states that a casualty that is moved within ten days of an operation is less likely to recover.

Theatre of Operations. The geographic area within which military operations are to take place.

Third Line Logistic Support. Where civilian transportation methods and practices become military. Normally found in the Forward Logistic Area about where the railway ends or beyond which it is tactically unwise to push loaded trains.

Transitional Operations. Operations which NATO defines as those that link the three Phases of War. (Advance to Contact, Meeting Engagements, Link-Up and Isolated Operations, Relief in Place, Forward and Rearward Passage of Lines.)

TRIAGE. The harsh, but necessary, military medical system for dividing casualties up into those that need immediate attention, those that can be tended to later and those on whom the limited medical effort could be wasted.

Underslung Loads. Loads to be carried beneath helicopters, normally in nets or by using special harnesses.

VTL. The French demountable load system. *See* **Demountable Loads.**

War Reserves. The reserves of equipment, personnel and ammunition needed to replace the losses sustained by an army at war. They are normally the product of **Battle Attrition Studies** and **Reviews of Rates and Scales.**

Notes

CHAPTER 1

(1) Field Marshal Wavell, *Speaking Generally*. (Macmillan, 1946.)
(2) Field Marshal Montgomery, *Memoirs*. (Collins, 1958).
(3) Shelby L. Stanton *The Rise and Fall of the American Army*. (Cloth Spar Books, 1989)
(4) Major General Julian Thompson, *The Lifeblood of War – Logistics in Armed Conflict*. (Brassey's, 1991).
(5) It was not only that the vessels had to reduce speed. Some were forced to hove-to completely. Some had to put into port for repairs. Deck cargo, normally vehicles and large International Standards Organisation containers, suffered; with a number being washed overboard as a result of the storm.
(6) Frederick William, the Great Elector, *Political Testament*.
(7) This tract is much beloved of British Army logisticians but its source and author have been difficult to trace. Certainly it has been around since the early 1970s. But it has always appeared anonymously!

CHAPTER 2

(1) Colonel General Golushko, Chief of Logistic Staff Red Army Armed Forces 1984: quoted in the British Army Staff College Camberley *Handbook on Logistics and Administration 1990*.
(2) '*Nobody in the British Army ever reads a regulation or an order as if it were to be a guide for his conduct, or in any other manner than as an amusing novel.*' The Lord Wellington, cited by R. D. Heinl Jr in *A Dictionary of Military and Naval Quotations*. (Naval Institute Press, 1966.)
(3) Brigadier M. White, British Army.

CHAPTER 4

(1) King Frederick II of Prussia: Instructions for his Generals. 1747. Cited by R. D. Heinl Jr in *A Dictionary of Military and Naval Quotations*. (Naval Institute Press, 1966.)
(2) Shelby L. Stanton, *The Rise and Fall of the American Army*. (Cloth Spar Books, 1989)

CHAPTER 5

(1) Von Moltke cited by R. D. Heinl Jr in *A Dictionary of Military and Naval Quotations*. (Naval Institute Press, 1966)
(2) The 1990 Germany Army trials of their 'MULTI' dismountable flat bed system showed that it could use the equivalent British (DROPS), French (VTL) and US (PLS) systems' flat racks.

(3) 1900 – Dark and start a two – hour load.

2100 – Start 80 km two – hour journey.

2300 – Start off-load at destination.

0100 – Start return trip.

0300 – Arrive at stocks. Insufficient time to make another return journey before daylight at 0500.

CHAPTER 7

(1) Admiral the Lord Nelson: Letter to Dr Mosely 1803. Cited by R. D. Heinl Jr in *A Dictionary of Military and Naval Quotations*. (Naval Institute Press, 1966.)

(2) John Keegan: *The Face of Battle*. (Jonathan Cape, 1976.)

(3) Captain MCM Bricknal RAMC: 'First Line Medical Support – The need for an Integrated Package', *The British Army Review*, No 98. August 1991, pp. 53–9

(4) The combined marine (who in the British Navy wear green berets) and airborne (who in the British Army wear maroon berets) medical facility was known as 'The Red and Green Life Machine'.

(5) Dr Jaase Evrin: 'Combat Stress and the Modern Soldier'. Quoted in the British Army 1990 Summer Tri-Service Study Period pamphlet *The Realities of War*.

(6) T. R. Mareth and A. E. Brooker: 'Combat Stress Reaction – A concept in Evolution', *Military Medicine* (No. 150. 1985.)

(7) *Ibid.*

(8) *Ibid.*

CHAPTER 8

(1) *Army Logistician*. Professional bulletin of United States Army logistics. (1991.)

(2) Bad weather and heavy useage caused the main forest track of one of the author's ammunition companies to become unusable. The engineer advice was that a heavy 'spreader' (a vehicle for laying aggregate evenly on a road surface) and a number of 'tipper' vehicles were needed before work could start. These specialist vehicles could not be made available for eight hours and work to repair the track could not start until then. Fortunately, the company had in support a weak platoon (20 men) of the Royal Pioneer Corps, the British Army's labour specialists. Using ordinary shovels and logs piled within the forest (and with the permission of the German wood's *Forstmeister!*) these 20 men constructed a corduroy log road on top of the track and after just two hours the ammunition convoys were rolling again.

CHAPTER 10

(1) B. Liddell Hart: *Thoughts on War*. (1944.) Cited by R. D. Heinl Jr in *A Dictionary of Military and Naval Quotations*. (Naval Institute Press, 1966.)

CHAPTER 11

(1) The author's personal experience.

CHAPTER 12

(1) The author's personal experience
(2) Mao Tse-tung: *On Guerilla Warfare*. (1937) Cited by R. D. Heinl Jr in 'A Dictionary of Military and Naval Quotations'. (Naval Institute Press, 1966.)

CHAPTER 13

(1) Orde Wingate: 'Recommendations for Wholly Air-Supplied Operations, Myitkyina Area, Burma, 1943'. Cited by R. D. Heinl Jr in *A Dictionary of Military and Naval Quotations*. (Naval Institute Press, 1966.)
(2) Lieutenant Colonel A. Taylor Royal Army Ordnance Corps, commanding officer of the British 3 Ordnance Battalion during the liberation of Kuwait 1991. Conversation with the author, September 1991.
(3) *Ibid.*
(4) The author, as a young petroleum platoon commander on exercise in Norway, did not know this. With no insulating layer, his petroleum 'pillow' tanks sank slowly into the ice. When the exercise ended and the tanks had been pumped empty of fuel, they could not be pulled from the ice without ripping them. A very understanding company commander arranged for the tanks to be watched over by a local Norwegian militia unit and organised things so that the young platoon comander could return to Norway for the spring thaw when the tanks could be safely pulled to the shore!
(5) Roman cartography did not allocate space on maps relative to distance on the ground. Instead, map distance was based on the amount of time it took to travel between two points. This produced maps which look strangely odd to the modern eye.

CHAPTER 14

(1) This quotation appeared in many British Army operations rooms in the build-up to the Coalition liberation of Kuwait 1991. Allegedly, it stemmed from discussions some two or three years earlier when the British were discussing the contents of their stockpile for what they called 'Out of Area' (ie. outside the NATO area). At that time it contained almost a brigade's worth of desert clothing and equipment. The requirement was queried and the clothing sold off, part of it to the Iraqi Army. When the first British soldiers and airmen deployed to Saudi Arabia in 1990, the British clothing industry had to produce completely new desert combat uniforms. They had to do so while ignoring the existing desert clothing patterns because uniforms in this style might be being worn by the Iraqi enemy! There is no official source for the quotation and it is probably apocryphal, used only to tease the civilian financiers whose thankless task it is to curb the more profligate and grandiose proposals of sailors, soldiers and airmen.
(2) Sir John Slessor: *Strategy for the West*, (1954.) Cited by R. D. Heinl Jr. in *A Dictionary of Military and Naval Quotations*. (Naval Institute Press. 1966.)
(3) General Patton: *War as I knew it*. Cited by R. D. Heinl Jr, in *A Dictionary of Military and Naval Quotations*. (Naval Institute Press 1966.)
(4) Civilian shipping may be available for deployment but, once hostilities start, reliance on national flag carriers will probably have to be made. As a rule of thumb, one British Royal Fleet Auxilliary replenishment vessel can carry enough to support one marine battalion for 30 days at low intensity rates. A modern division has 9–12 manoeuvre units which, with divisional troops, equates to a requirement for between 12 and 15

vessels. It is difficult to be more precise because much depends on the resources available in-theatre and the size of the ships concerned.

(5) Charcoal is used as part of the filtering system for most Western nuclear, biological and chemical defence equipment. The Iraqi potential for chemical warfare caused most of the armies involved in the liberation of Kuwait to review their scales of these equipments. More importantly, the threat of 'SCUD' rocket-delivered chemical munitions in civilian population centres forced many Middle Eastern governments into hasty attempts to protect their civilian populations by rapidly equipping them with respirators and the like. The effect of all this buying was to make charcoal a scarce commodity indeed.

(6) It is sometimes forgotten that the three-battalion-strong infantry regiment of a German Panzer division had only enough personnel carriers to transport one battalion. One of the remaining battalions could be carried in soft-skin wheeled vehicles and the other had to march on its feet.

(7) K Macksey: *For Want of a Nail – The Impact of War on Logistics and Communications.* (Brassey's, 1989.)

CHAPTER 15

(1) The Lord Wellington: Letter of 28 January 1811, cited by R. D. Heinl Jr. in 'A *Dictionary of Military and Naval Quotations'.* (Naval Institute Press, 1966.)

(2) K Macksey: *For Want of a Nail – The Impact of War on Logistics and Communications.* (Brasseys, 1989.)

(3) Almost all of the liberation of Kuwait officers interviewed by the author mentioned this aspect, largely in respect to locally hired labour. But no unclassified documentary evidence seems to exist and none of the officers concerned were willing to be quoted.

(4) M. Glover: *The Fight for the Channel Ports: Calais to Brest 1940 – A Study in confusion.* 90. (Leo Cooper in association with Secker & Warburg, 1985.) There was the very honourable exception of three French crane drivers.

(5) Field Marshal Rommel cited by R. D. Heinl Jr. in *A Dictionary of Military and Naval Quotations.* (Naval Institute Press, 1966.)

Bibliography

Barnett, Correlli. *Britain And Her Army 1509–1970: A Military, Political and Social Survey*. A Lane (Penguin). 1970. *The Collapse of British Power*. Eyre Methuen. 1972. *The Audit of War: The Illusion and Reality of Britain as a Great Nation*. Macmillans. 1986.

Chambers, James. *The Devil's Horsemen – The Mongol Invasion of Europe*. Weidenfeld and Nicolson. 1988.

Chandler, David G. *The Campaigns of Napoleon*. Macmillan. 1966.

Clayton, Anthony. *Three Marshals of France – Leadership After Trauma*. Brassey's. 1992.

Cooper, Mathew and Lucas, James. *Panzer, The Armoured Force of the Third Reich*. St Martin's Press. 1976.

Dinter, Elmar and Griffith, Paddy. *Not over by Christmas. NATO's Central Front in World War III*. Anthony Bird Publications, Hippocrene Books Inc. 1983.

Dixon, Norman F. *On the Psychology of Military Incompetence*. Jonathan Cape. 1976.

Duffy, Christopher. *The Army of Maria Theresa, The Armed Forces of Imperial Austria 1740–1780*. David and Charles. 1977. *The Army of Frederick The Great*. Purnell Book Services Ltd. 1974.

Dupuy, Colonel T N. *Numbers, Predictions and War*. MacDonald and Jane's. 1979.

Fay, Sir Sam. *The War Office at War*. Hutchinson. 1937.

Fortescue. *The Early History of Transport and Supply*. London University Press. 1928.

Fraser, General David. *And We Shall Shock Them, The British Army in the Second World War*. Hodder and Stoughton. 1983.

Glover, Michael. *The Fight For The Channel Ports, Calais To Brest 1940: A Study In Confusion*. Leo Cooper in association with Secker & Warburg. 1985.

Guderian, General Heinz. *Panzer Leader*. Michael Joseph. 1952.

Hamilton, Nigel. *Monty, The Making of a General 1887–1942*. Hamish Hamilton Ltd. 1981.

Herzog, Major General Chaim. *The War of Atonement*. Weidenfeld and Nicolson. 1975.

Kennedy, Paul. *The Rise and Fall of the Great Powers*. Unwin Hyman Ltd. 1988.

Macksey, Kenneth. *For Want of a Nail*. Brassey's (UK). 1989.

Pagonis, Lieutenant General William G with Cruikshank, Jeffrey L. *Moving Mountains. Lessons in Leadership and Logistics from the Gulf War*. Harvard Business School Press. 1992.

Robinson, General C W. *Wellington's Campaigns, Peninsular – Waterloo 1808–1815*. Hugh Rees Ltd. 1907.

Sinclair, Joseph. *Arteries of War. A History of Military Transportation*. Airlife Publishing Ltd. 1992.

Slim, Field Marshal W. *Defeat Into Victory*. Cassell. 1956.

Thompson, Major General Julian. *The Lifeblood of War: Logistics in Armed Conflict*. Brassey's. 1990.

Van Crefeld, Martin. *Supplying War, Logistics from Wallenstein to Patton.* Cambridge University Press. 1977. *Technology and War.* Free Press. 1989.

Various. *Operation Granby, An Account Of The Gulf Crisis 1990–1991 and the British Army's Contribution To The Liberation of Kuwait.* UK Government Publication. 1991.

Von Manstein, Field Marshal Erich. *Lost Victories.* Methuen & Co Ltd. 1958.

Index